Behind the Dim Unknown

Behind the Dim Unknown

TWENTY-SIX NOTABLE SCIENTISTS FACE
A HOST OF UNSOLVED PROBLEMS
AND UNITEDLY REACH A CONCLUSION

EDITED BY *John Clover Monsma*

G. P. PUTNAM'S SONS   NEW YORK

Copyright © 1966 by Dr. John Clover Monsma

Library of Congress Catalogue Card Number: 66-15587

PRINTED IN THE UNITED STATES OF AMERICA

CONTENTS

5]

. . . behind the dim unknown
Standeth God within the shadow,
Keeping watch above His own.

—JAMES RUSSELL LOWELL

Behind the Dim Unknown

EDITOR'S INTRODUCTION

WHEN Napoleon was crossing the Mediterranean for his great military campaign in Egypt he had a mighty bad time of it. The General was troubled by almost continual seasickness. Most of the time he was lying on deck, a coarse pillow under his head, and only occasionally, when the sea was not too boisterous, did he ask his friend Bourrienne to read to him. One of the books used was the Bible.

Toward the end of the long voyage the weather moderated, and the General arranged for evening talks with his scientists that were on board—chemists, mineralogists, geologists, astronomers, and engineers. This was nothing new. In his home in Paris gatherings of scientists had been held quite frequently. He ordered the meetings held on deck.

One evening the scientists again grouped themselves around Napoleon while he was reclining. Somehow the discussion turned philosophical, and before long the learned men—all partisans of the Revolution, disciples of Voltaire and associates—began to agree with great Gallic gusto and much gesturing that creation of the cosmos by a God was old-fashioned nonsense and that very shortly natural science would solve all—"literally all"—problems to the minutest detail.

The General had not said a word, but while the men were talking and scoffing and nodding their heads vehemently in agreement he not only had been listening, but also had been looking upward, staring at the multitude of bright stars in that oriental sky.

Suddenly he sat up, looked at the loudest and most voluble talkers among them, and then asked in that resonant voice of his, as he pointed to the stars, "And who made those?

Did natural science make them? Did they make themselves? Did they just happen? But that would be very unscientific! Gentlemen, I don't agree with you at all—not at all!"

The rest of the incident is unknown and, if known, would be immaterial for our purpose. All I should like to add is that belief and disbelief still take the same stance a century and a half after Napoleon's day and will continue to do so until He who is the Truth will be both seen and heard, suddenly, overpoweringly, by all men, without distinction.

As of now, disbelief is making by far the greater impact.

The book I am here introducing will seek in some small way to neutralize that impact, here and there.

I hope the reader will permit a few additional observations about the book.

Not much time has elapsed since I edited a book entitled *The Evidence of God in an Expanding Universe.* That book dealt with the *existence* of God. A large group of recognized natural scientists set forth in it, briefly and clearly, the reasons for their acceptance, as scientists, of a Divine Creator and Sustainer of the universe.

The present volume deals with the *greatness* of God as evidenced by the problems that scientists encounter in their study of nature. Another group of natural scientists, all men of scholarly rank and filling responsible positions, seek to explain in laymen's language how such problems constitute a testimony of Divine greatness—intellectual and creative greatness—that is not only fascinating but also truly overpowering in its eloquence.

Personally I feel that there is nothing that can give one such a deeply moving perception of the infinitude of God and the comparative puniness of man as a thoughtful look at these problems. And there are plenty of them! In fact, they are numberless. Many have been solved. Very many others are still unsolved. There are also a large number that to all present appearances are completely unsolvable.

A mere consideration of the length of time that was required to make up the solved group of problems is impressive. If one figures from classical Greek times—say, from Pythagoras' initial flounderings—it took scientific man twenty-five centuries to arrive where he now finds himself. Surely, a creative mind of awesome depth and power must account for that.

The many problems that finally have been unraveled and whose solution has resulted in so much speculative and practical good, especially in the past half century, are indicative of a conceptive, originating power that reels the human mind and stuns the imagination. And is not man's ingenuity, which enabled him laboriously but successfully to work out these problems, another spire pointing to a source omniscient?

But we are still dealing with preliminaries. By consensus of the best modern minds the problems that have been solved are a small group compared with the legion of unsolved ones. We are only at the beginning of the exploratory road. Natural scientists have gone only a short distance, and the long stretches before them, the vistas to the right and the left and into the hazy distance, are crowded with problems that seem impenetrable and unyielding. And among these unsolved ones, so at least many of the scientists say, are the ultramysterious ones whose intrinsic secrets the Creator seems determined to keep for himself and that very likely will never be detected and analyzed by mortal man.

All this, of course, leads to a realization of man's extremely limited knowledge, also in the field of natural science. Pretentiousness is ruled out. There remains only thankfulness for the opportunity to think at least some of God's thoughts after Him and thus to gain added incentives not only to adore Him but also, by His gracious favor, to enrich our own little finite lives. With these two objectives in mind—the major and the minor—may our scientists continue their diligent searchings and still add to their modest acquisitions.

*   *   *

The fact of man's greatly limited, really embryonic knowledge frequently leads to uncertainty and fear, especially when minds are centered on such branches of natural science as chemistry, nuclear physics, and astrophysics. There are times when not only the generality of thinking people but also some of the grand seigneurs among the world's chemists and physicists do a bit of silent, unnoticed quavering in their inmost parts when they reflect on the great physical powers that already have been released in recent years and on the much greater, far-ranging, and violently cataclysmic powers that may sooner or later be released, designedly or inadvertently. Dread phantasms of a world shattered, of humanity incinerated, or even of the solar system reduced to cosmic dust and ashes occasionally float before mental eyes grown wide.

But nothing of the kind will happen—not if the Bible is more than a collection of beautiful and fanciful literature. Any terminal blow of a terrestrial or cosmic nature will not be due to the manipulations of man. It will be due solely to special Divine intervention. Even then such an occurrence should not engender fear—not if one is on good terms with the Supreme Disposer.

The age-old doctrine of Divine Providence—believed in by Protestants, Roman Catholics, Eastern Orthodox, Jews, and Mohammedans—should buttress souls and minds. No one, I think, has given simpler, yet more beautiful, expression to that doctrine than James Russell Lowell:

> . . . behind the dim unknown
> Standeth God within the shadow,
> Keeping watch above His own.

The New England poet, in using the phrase "dim unknown," had the unforeseeable changes and seeming vagaries of history in mind. I am taking the liberty to apply this same cryptic, yet pregnant, phrase to the natural science field. This field, too, is to an almost incredible extent a "dim unknown." But God stands behind it, within the shadow, watching. He is watching His own sovereign possession, watching unceasingly. And so: "The Lord reigneth; let the earth rejoice. . . ." (Ps. 97:1, AV) In choosing the first of Dr. Lowell's three lines just quoted for the title of this volume, I mean to stress with great pointedness these same truths and facts.

In going through this book, I know that the readers will find the large and sundry array of unsolved problems not only impressive and fascinating, but also humbling. They affected me that way; I cannot help believing that our readers will share my response. And it will be remembered, of course, that the problems here presented are but a fraction of the totality of such problems.

*　　*　　*

So far as editorial management of the book is concerned, it seemed best to divide the abundant material into a number of small divisions, each dealing with a separate branch of natural science. In the first part of the book there are two writers for each division; in the second part, one writer. We have insisted on scientists and writers of quality and have been satisfied with nothing less.

I wish to express publicly my cordial thanks to the writers. They are men of great learning; they fill prominent positions; they are exceedingly busy. But they saw the high value, in these shifting, skeptical, faithless times, of a straightforward deposition of the truth as they saw it. So they got busy, most of them burning the midnight oil.

I am grateful. And so, I trust, will be our readers.

JOHN CLOVER MONSMA

THE WONDER OF LIFE AND ITS ENDLESS VARIETIES

BY RUSSELL C. ARTIST

BIOLOGIST
BOTANIST

Dr. Artist received his education in the United States and in Europe. He has a B.Sc. degree from Butler University, an M.Sc. from Northwestern University, and a Ph.D. from the University of Minnesota. Afterward he pursued extensive graduate studies at the University of Zurich, Switzerland, and for five years was a professor at Frankfurt-am-Main College, Germany. For the last twelve years he has been the head of the Department of Biology at David Lipscomb College. He is well known in both biological and botanical circles as a keen and penetrating researcher and a man of great facility in the latest biologic theories and discoveries. Among his several monographs are Pollen Spectrum Studies *and* Bog Pollen Analysis. *Dr. Artist is a member of three state academies of science: Indiana, Tennessee, and Texas.*

BIOLOGY is the science of life. This writer is a biologist, and he is the creationist type of biologist.

When the Apostle Paul prepared himself for his missionary journeys, he found himself in a scientific world that he knew only too well. At rather an early age he had absorbed much of the thoughts and teachings of the great minds of his day. Tarsus, in Cilicia, his birthplace, was a great intellectual center, and he had made full use of his opportunities. The contents of his Epistles bear that out.

Paul had heard much about Aristotle, the Greek philosopher, and about Virgil, the Roman scientist and poet, and about other philosophers, scientists, and poets, and most of these had told the limited number of the intelligentsia of that age, among other things, that life itself was something problematic, but that they were convinced that in the beginning it had come into existence by itself, spontaneously, by generation of living matter from nonliving. In other words, life had just happened.

The Apostle took a different stance. For him the great problem of the *origin* of life was also solved, but in a different way. In fact, it had never been a problem at all. He was to write to the Colossians, very simply: "By him (God) were all things created . . ." (Ch. 1:16, AV), and he was to expand on the statement with a quiet but firm conviction.

This writer follows the Apostle in his beliefs and assertions, humbly but with resolution. I don't believe that our natural life just happened. And I believe that my position is entirely up-to-date, even in our age of subcellular particles, such as genes, chromosomes, and nucleic acids. Our DNA (chemical substance) is certainly not the secret of life. It is but a sub-unit of a living cell, and although it may be an amazing factory for synthesis (combination) of many kinds of elements, it is still useless by itself. DNA molecules did not precede the cell, but both have existed from the beginning. Rather than DNA being the secret of life, life is the secret of DNA.

This takes us back to life itself. The *origin* of life is no problem. But life itself is indeed a problem. It's an unsolved problem—one of the greatest. Man has never understood its real essence, its intrinsic nature, the secret of its dynamism. So it remains a wonder, incomprehensible but precious. It remains part of "the dim unknown" behind which God, the Divine Creator and Watchman, is standing.

Although life in its ultimate sense is a mystery, biologists can study the physical composition, laws, properties, functions, and relationships of its varied habitations. And both biologists and men in general can admire and wonder at the countless ways in which life has been made to burgeon forth. The diversity of its manifestations in all living organisms—men, animals, vegetation—is inconceivable, and it all bespeaks an endlessly diversified Divine mind and the concurrent, effective use of Divine power.

Let me illustrate this wonderful diversity by just a few examples. Let me call the reader's attention to just four little but very interesting examples—four out of a million—culled from a world usually hidden from our sight. Suppose we begin with a human being when he starts out on what we casually call life's journey.

Wonders and Problems at Time of Birth

In the very act of being born every human being gives a remarkable demonstration of the fact that we are "fearfully and wonderfully made" (Ps. 139:14, AV) and at the same time points up a problem in biology for which there can be no adequate explanation other than that there are of necessity intelligent planning and design.

The average person on the street knows, of course, that his heart is like a double pump, the right side containing impure blood and the left side containing only pure or oxygenated blood, which has come from the lungs. Two separate systems of circulation keep the two types of blood from mixing. The right side is called the systemic system and the left side the pulmonary system. The adult heart is thus arranged to keep these two completely separated in order for the body to function properly.

But the unborn child has no need for this complete separation of the two types of blood. The mother does the breathing for the embryo (the lungs are not even inflated in the unborn child), and the mother's bloodstream provides for the aeration of the child's blood. Thus, there are two short circuits in the system of circulation of the embryo before birth. One of these is a small opening between the right auricle and the left auricle of the fetal heart—an opening right through the wall, known as the *foramen ovale,* which allows the blood to flow uninterrupted through the two cavities. The other bypass in the system is a short and thick vessel, equipped with a tough sheet of smooth muscle, which connects the pulmonary artery with the great aortic arch that carries oxygenated blood to all parts of the body. These two short circuits, prepared to serve the unborn fetus, are destined to be changed at the time of birth and are never used again.

The sequence and precision of it all are wonders in themselves and, with God ruled out, problems of considerable dimensions. With God recognized, they become parts of His creational design.

The opening between the two auricles, the *foramen ovale,* is in embryonic life guarded by flaps of tissue that permit the flow of blood through the opening. At birth, and instantaneously, because of certain pressure relationships, the flaps are closed, never to open again. The exact nature of these pressure relationships is not known. We are facing an unsolved problem. Eventually new tissue grows across the opening, and in the majority of people this shortcut is completely sealed off in adult life. Otherwise, there would be a condition called leakage of the heart, which would mean a mixing of pure and impure blood. In about one-fifth of the population, however, a tiny opening remains to mark the spot of this shortcut that once existed before birth. It is indeed a marvel of unique design that can provide for a system that operates efficiently through embryonic life and then, at the moment of birth, causes a closing of this opening so that it remains sealed throughout adult life.

Now we come to the muscle that *contracts only once* during the entire duration of life. It is the same smooth muscle which occurs on the short bypass from the pulmonary artery to the aorta. As soon as the lungs fill with air at the moment of birth, the contracting muscle causes the vessel to close off completely. This causes the blood to flood into the lungs to be aerated with oxygen. The action of the muscle is effected by some unknown stimulus—one of our unsolved problems. The muscle eventually degenerates and disappears.

After birth the breathing and circulation are similar to those of the adult body. One could not find a better example of wise planning and intelligent design than in these two adjustments, which are made by every fetus at birth.

That it is absolutely essential for the two to function properly—without training or research—lies in the sobering fact that after failure there are no second chances. As the lungs have not inflated before in the unborn child, there must be no slipup in this at the time when the baby must breathe for itself. Also, that these two shortcuts should be closed correctly the *first and only time* means the difference between life and death.

Parents who await the birth of their child can derive strength and joy from the knowledge that in the vast majority of cases God's creational design works out wonderfully and that for Him problems do not exist.

The Spider That Lives in a Diving Bell

Spiders are air-breathing creatures that have invaded almost every habitat known to exist in which such creatures can make a home, but there is one spider that, strangely enough, habitually makes its home in that most inhospitable of all environments for spiders—the water! This spider, the *Argyroneta aquatica*, displays the curious instinct of building her nest below the surface of the water, and it is somewhat in the fashion of a diving bell, such as that which men have lately fashioned for their ocean research. The animal usually selects still and untroubled water for her purpose. First, she spins a balloon-shaped nest of cobweb, an oval hollow lined with delicate silk. It is anchored by strands of web to some nearby plant or other object under the surface of the water. The diving bell, which is open below, allows the entrance and egress of the mistress that made it. But it is not yet ready to be occupied, for it must now be supplied with fresh air—first, to displace the water present inside of it and, second, to breathe.

The hind legs of the spider are so delicately covered with hair that she can take hold of an air bubble, take it down into the water, and release it underneath the diving bell which she made. The bubble naturally rises to the surface, displacing an equal amount of water. This process is continued until the bell is completely filled with air. It then becomes apparent that all this ingenious and unorthodox behavior is for the purpose of providing for her young. Eggs are laid in the uppermost part—the ceiling of the bell. When they hatch, a fresh supply of air is always at hand, and they are completely safe from any air-breathing enemies by a cover of water.

In this oval bell, which is a silk-lined cell open below, she watches for prey, such as aquatic insects. Having stocked her larder full of these delicacies, she closes the opening and spends the winter, with plenty of food and air both for herself and for her progeny.

Let us consider these intricate adjustments for life underwater. In order to live such a life as this, the spider must be able to secrete a web that is completely waterproof and airtight—no small feat in itself! The matter of carrying the water bubbles to fill the diving bell is still more amazing. It would be difficult for me to say how to carry a water bubble, but this spider does it, time and time again—without one mishap! It has been said that "she descends with her bubble like with a globe of quicksilver."

How does she know how many bubbles to bring into her nest? Who taught her to carry the bubbles of air? How, indeed, did she ever come by the idea of living under the surface of the water? Unsolvable problems? Yes and no.

Such a highly specialized type of existence, with the

equally specialized organs for providing for this unusual life, defy any satisfactory explanation except that this species of spider was designed, indeed *created*, this way. The only logical, adequate explanation is that an intelligent being designed the water spider for this extraordinary kind of life. Since it all had to be done perfectly the first time, there could be no error in any of these intricacies, or there just would not have been any more water spiders.

God's purpose? Chiefly, His own Divine enjoyment: "The Lord shall rejoice in his works." (Ps. 104:31, AV) And He gives man the high privilege of joining Him therein—in man-like measure.

The Yucca Flower and the Pronuba Moth

Another example of life's God-created diversity is the inter-dependence of the yucca flower of the Southwest and the *Pronuba* moth, a silvery insect of the same region and quite different from the clothes moth against which our house-wives wage their unending war.

The yucca plant grows in Texas and in some of the deserts of the Southwest. Sometimes it is called the Spanish bayonet, a fitting name, as anyone who has grasped its long, slender, but spiny leaves will testify. In the springtime, from the center of a rosette of leaves near the ground there appears a tall flower stalk, anywhere from two to six feet in height, which bears a great mass of large showy white flowers. The flower produces pollen which is too heavy for wind pollination. Besides, hanging down as the flower does, no pollen can fall into it. This is where the female of the *Pronuba* moth (*Pronuba yuccasella*) comes into the picture.

She goes about to complete her mission of pollinating the flowers just as if she were aware of the fact that the flowers of this species have stigmas that hang downward and that the sensitive stigmatic surface which receives the pollen from the stamens is inside the hollow. In the economy of the desert her instinct has been designed to provide survival for the yucca, as well as for her own larvae. Neither the plant nor the insect could exist without the other.

Pollen is gathered by the moth in specialized mouthparts, fixed into a pellet or wad and carried with her as she visits flower after flower. First, she crawls up the downward-pointing style to the bulbous ovary, the place where the seeds will develop if the ovules are fertilized. In this soft bulb she lays her eggs by piercing it with her ovipositor.

What about the wad of pollen? Well, now she does a very surprising thing. Instead of flying off after she has laid her eggs, she crawls back down along the style to the stigma, at the end of the style, and there she proceeds to pack the stigma full of pollen with the pellet which she has brought from another flower. Strangely enough, she has taken care of providing for her own offspring, as well as for the reproduction of the yucca flower. The flower really does benefit by this arrangement, for in spite of the fact that the young of the *Pronuba* moth do feed on some of the seeds that develop in the ovary, of the 200 or so produced, only about 20 will be eaten by the larvae of the moth. So there are plenty of seeds left for propagating the yucca plant.

That the two organisms are completely dependent on each other is attested by the fact that all the ripe seedpods of the yucca show one or more scars where the moth punctured them in laying her eggs. Any pods which are not thus pierced fail to set seed. The moth has not visited the flower, pollen has not been crammed into the stigmatic tube, and no fertilization has occurred. Besides, without the yucca the larvae of the moth would have no suitable feeding place.

When fully developed after having fed on the seeds developed in the seedpod, the larvae eat their way out, drop by a silken cord to the ground, then, in the ground, spin a tight cocoon around themselves, and wait—wait all year until the yucca flower blooms again!

As for the female *Pronuba,* her whole destiny and purpose is to fertilize the yucca and to deposit her eggs in the right place for the larvae to feed on and grow. When that is done, she dies. Unbiased reason, plain common sense, must tell us that the *Pronuba* moth and the yucca flower are not the result of an accident or a chance association of two interdependent organisms. The Creator must have brought both into existence at the same time, for without the moth the yucca could not be pollinated, and without the yucca the moth could not provide for her larvae.

Between a problem that is definitely beyond solution and an infinite Creator-God, the choice should not be difficult.

The Case of the Spanish Copris Beetle

The Spanish *Copris* is a beetle with a heavy and cumbersome body and a horn of good size on her head. The legs of this beetle are short and stubby and seemingly unfit for kneading and rolling, as the pill-roller beetles do. The manner in which this insect goes about the business of preparing food for her young has never been adequately explained. The problem of the radical change in her habits, from a glutton with an insatiable hunger for food into a starving, unselfish provisioner of food for her young, is still to be solved.

May or June of each year is our beetle's egg-laying time. She is a scavenger beetle and has her nesting place in some heap of refuse from a barnyard. She has burrowed under the heap, made a nice roomy spot, and now begins to carry food in—plenty of it and all of it pretty moist. A narrow passage is left for her to get in and out, but for the rest the room is almost filled with the shapeless mass of food.

Then, like a baker who kneads his dough by hand, the Spanish *Copris* begins to press and knead this little mass (it's little; after all, she herself is little). She tamps and presses it with her short stubby legs. Then she divides it into equal parts and makes each part into a little cake. When all that is done, she proceeds with the matter of egg laying. A single egg is placed on each little cake, and some of the material is wrapped around the egg. After about twenty-four hours the egg-depositing operation is done. There is usually no fixed number of cakes.

Now it would seem that she could leave the burrow in search of some food for herself, for she has been going hungry all this time. She wouldn't think of touching the food that is meant for her young. But she stays right where she is. In fact, she stays another *four months* until every one of the eggs has hatched! "Her clumsy horn-shod foot is more sensitive in the dark than the sight of a man in broadest daylight," said Fabre, the late and famous French entomologist.

Now she hears her grubs hatching. She hustles from one tiny nest to another. Apparently she has no instinct for demolishing the little cake in case the grub (a wormlike larva) gets stuck and fails to make its exit; her instinct seems to be solely for the building and repairing of her larger quarters. Some people have scoffed at the ingenious manner in which this lowly scavenger of the field goes about her business. They argue that the *Copris* stays in her burrow during all this time for the simple reason that she cannot get out—because of weakness, obstruction, or what not. But some people are wrong! The *Copris* does not dream of leaving. She keeps her little home intact, removes any debris that might fall on the little nests, and goes about polishing and inspecting. And she goes hungry for four long months, whereas before she was a glutton, eating voraciously and constantly.

When the grubs finally emerge, she sees to it that each one is supplied with a generous supply of food—plenty and enough to last until all are able to shift for themselves. Then she begins to think about herself. She has been true to her God-implanted instinct. And the reader and this writer have been witnesses to love among the beetles—mother love!

I have finished presenting to the reader a few illustrations of the marvels and diversities of natural life. When one remembers that these illustrations could be multiplied a million times, one is bound to stand amazed to the point of speechlessness. I am humble and honest enough to believe that, for an explanation of all this, both soul- and mind-less nature and fortuity are ruled out; that an omniscient God alone is the answer.

DECIPHERING THE CODE THAT BEARS THE SECRETS OF LIFE

BY ALBERT M. WINCHESTER

BIOLOGIST

GENETICIST

In American biology circles Dr. Winchester is definitely a front-rank man. After he had obtained M.A. and Ph.D. degrees from the University of Texas, he pursued post-graduate studies and did research work at the University of Chicago, Harvard University, the University of Michigan, and the University of Munich, Germany. He was a professor of biology at Baylor University and the chairman of the Department of Biology at Stetson University, and he is presently a professor of biology at Colorado State College. Dr. Winchester is the author of three textbooks —on biology, zoology, and genetics—and he has written popular volumes on human heredity and related topics. He has also written the biology sections of several standard encyclopedias, including the Britannica. *He is the past president of the Florida Academy of Science, and his specialty is genetics, particularly human genetics.*

Of all the great scientific discoveries of modern times there is none that has given greater evidence of God's handiwork than the deciphering of the genetic code, which tells us the way in which all forms of life on the earth grow and carry on their varied activities. It is as if man had suddenly been given the power to translate God's messages telling the secrets of life, messages that are written in a complex code that until recent times resisted all man's efforts to understand it.

This does not mean that all the deciphering has been completed. But it does mean that at long last the code is beginning to yield its mysteries to the probing minds of the biological scientists. Much of the language remains hidden in "the dim unknown," but we have made an encouraging beginning of understanding it. None of man's discoveries can equal this one as a convincing argument for Divine planning and direction of growth for the myriad forms of life that inhabit this earth.

This language of life, as we have just stated, is in the form of a genetic code, which is not greatly unlike the coded magnetic tapes that have become such an important part of our age of computers. It is a code that forms a central thread of unity, giving a common bond which ties together all forms of life. From a tiny flea on a dog, seeking a drop of blood, on which its life depends, to the highly complex body of a human being, all living objects share this code, this common language. Man-made languages vary greatly, and even the great linguists can understand but a fraction of the thousands of languages that have sprung up in the course of history. God's language, on the other hand, is universal; once the code is understood, its message can be understood by all.

It is the genetic code of the language of life that tells the microscopic embryo within an acorn how to utilize the water and minerals from the soil, the carbon dioxide from the air, and the energy of the sunlight to construct a huge oak tree towering high in the air and with branches spreading far outward to the sides. The code within the seed from a pine tree has a slightly different message; it also produces a tree, but a tree that is easily distinguished from the oak. There is never a mix-up in the understanding of the message; a pine tree never grows from an acorn.

The same language, but with a different message, is found

within the embryo growing in a female cat. This message tells the embryo how to utilize the food and oxygen that are being received from its mother's body so that a kitten is formed. The message is never misread so that a puppy is formed instead, even though the female cat eats the same food as a female dog that is expecting puppies. This is the language of life, which causes all living things to reproduce according to their kind. This was first mentioned in the Book of Genesis, but we are just now beginning to understand. We see the results of the transmission of messages through the language of life so often that we come to accept it as commonplace, but there has never been a miracle equal to this one, which takes place each time a new life develops.

What is this great language of life? It is a language that has come down through the generations since the beginning of life on earth, a language that predates the oldest human language. Yet it has certain similarities to the letters, words, and sentences that make up modern languages. It is a language that has required all of man's ingenuity and modern microscopic and chemical techniques to penetrate down to the fine structure of a cell, on which the messages are imprinted.

Perhaps we can better visualize these messages if we reduce ourselves down to a size where we can see and read them as we would read the printed pages of a book. The messages are contained within the nucleus of cells, and since cells are microscopic in size, we ourselves must be prepared for a great reduction. Suppose we use some marvelous chemical that has the power to reduce us to one-tenth our size each time it is applied. Suppose you are five feet tall and use this chemical once. You will now be reduced to a Lilliputian dwarf only six inches tall, but you will still be much too large to see clearly cells and their contents. Apply the chemical a second time, and you are only half an inch tall. Now the cells become visible, but they are still too small for you to see and read the messages within. Once more the chemical is applied, and you are now only five-hundredths of an inch tall.

Still another treatment, and you become an infinitesimal speck—only five-thousandths of an inch tall. But it is only in this greatly reduced size that you can see and appreciate the intricate details of cell structure. You are now seeing things with your naked eye that man, in his normal size, has been able to see only with the aid of extremely high-powered microscopes.

Cells in different parts of the human body appear quite different in shape and general external appearance; but they all contain the same basic parts, and the same messages of life are written within each cell. Hence, it makes little difference which type of cell we have chosen for closer examination. One from the liver will do very well. This cell to you, in your greatly reduced size, will seem about the size of a basketball. It will have a transparent cover, so you can see inside it. You see that the cell is filled with a thick syrupy fluid, which is in constant motion, flowing around inside the cell. Within this fluid you see many suspended bodies, the most prominent of them being the nucleus, which is about the size of a large grapefruit near the center of the cell.

Now we come to the heart of the matter. The nucleus contains the messages in which we are interested, so let us examine its contents. Much of the nucleus is filled with very long and slender structures about the diameter—as we are seeing them, in our greatly reduced size—of coarse sewing thread. These are the chromosomes, which bear the genes, and it is the genes which carry the messages of life. There are 46 of these chromosomes in the nucleus, so in order to see one of them more clearly, let us remove it from the nucleus. Tightly wound around the outside of the thread are tiny coiled bodies, each in the shape of a long flexible ladder twisted about itself rather tightly. These are the genes. One gene may have as many as 30,000 rungs on its ladder; yet this gene will represent only one sentence in the language of life, and there must be thousands of sentences in order to convey the information needed for the construction of a human body. What about that?

All the genes look very much alike, yet careful examination shows that the rungs on the ladders are of 4 different kinds. Each rung type represents 1 letter in the alphabet of life. There are 26 letters in the alphabet of the English language, and you may be wondering how it is possible for many messages to be written with an alphabet of only 4 letters. This is no problem. In fact, 2 letters are sufficient to write any word in any language, as witnessed by the fact that the Morse code has only 2 symbols (letters), and we use this code everyday to transmit messages of all kinds. Various combinations of dots and dashes are all that is needed. All the words in the language of life are 3-letter words, and again this would seem to limit the sentences which could be formed. But we must remember that one sentence may be up to 10,000 words in length. A man writing such sentences using 3-letter words from a 4-letter alphabet could write for his entire lifetime without beginning to touch on the many possible kinds of sentences that could be formed. Hence, every living thing on earth can have its own peculiar variety of messages on its genes, and each living thing can be an individual that is not exactly like any other.

There is one notable exception. Identical twins, triplets, and higher multiple births in man, as well as other forms of life, all start life as a single cell with a single set of messages. Each time the cell divides, the messages are duplicated exactly and passed to the two cells that are formed by the division. During early embryonic life these cells become separated. If they separate into two parts, then two separate living beings are formed. Each, therefore, will carry the same messages in their chromosomes and will be alike in all the features which are controlled by the genes of heredity.

Once man had gained some insight into the language of life, he turned his attention to trying to learn how the cells read the messages so that they grow according to the information contained in the messages. The bodies which construct the protoplasm (the material of which the cells are made) lie outside the nucleus. How can they know what

[34

messages lie on the chromosomes inside the nucleus? The information is transmitted by means of messengers, which pass from the chromosomes to the construction bodies. The messages may be compared with printed instructions which come off the master printing plate in the nucleus. These messages are destroyed in the process of their use in the cell, but more printed instructions can be received from the master copy, which remains safe within the nucleus. Again we have a striking illustration of Divine planning in arranging for the language of life.

One sentence in the language of life directs the construction of one specific kind of protein material, and protein is the basic material of which living protoplasm is made. Since no two living objects receive exactly the same kind of message, no two living objects have exactly the same kinds of protein within their cells, with the exception of the multiple births mentioned above. This becomes apparent when we try to transplant tissues or organs from one person to another. If the proteins do not match the proteins of the person receiving the transplant, there will be a rejection of the transplanted tissue or organ. By very special techniques we have been able to transplant kidneys in recent years, but to do this, we must depress the rejection mechanism of the body. If a person needing a kidney transplant is fortunate enough, however, to have an identical twin, there is no problem. He will accept the transplant as readily as he will accept a transplant of tissue from his own body.

Thus, we see that man has gone a considerable distance in understanding the language of life, but this understanding has been attended by the discovery of a host of problems still unsolved. Note, for example, a few of these problems:

All the messages that we have referred to cannot be read and acted on at the same time. What is it that does the regulating?

What tells the genes for eyes, for example, to settle in the place for eyes, not, say, at the bottom of one's foot?

What tells the genes to operate at the proper time and place, not at other times and places?

Who or what are the messengers that travel from the chromosomes *inside* the cell nucleus to the construction bodies *outside?* What is the organizing force in the cell that makes such messengers function properly and adequately?

In the case of human beings, is there a special cellular or chromosomal preparation for future psychophysical contacts, such as those between the brain and the soul?

The questions and problems can, of course, be multiplied. New problems rise constantly. This is especially true when scientists go into the more intricate technical details.

We have discovered some of the great secrets of life, and we are thankful. We have begun to understand the language of life—a fact of great magnitude. But we find that the further we penetrate into God's plan for the transmission of information about growth in living matter, the more we recognize its great complexity, and the more we realize the Divine intelligence that was required to work out such a plan.

It is as if we were permitted a glimpse into a great library, with a chance to look at a few pages in books which have been opened to us, but with the great body of information still hidden from our finite minds. So much remains hidden in "the dim unknown," yet our brief glimpses into some of the open pages have given us a great reverence for the mass of information contained in the library as a whole.

The more we *finite* men search and explore, the more we feel compelled to exclaim with the ancient poet-prophet: "Great is our Lord, and of great power; his understanding (intelligence, knowledge) is *infinite.*" (Ps. 147:5, AV)

PRESENT ATTEMPTS TO CREATE LIFE IN A TEST TUBE

BY DUANE T. GISH

BIOCHEMIST

Dr. Gish is one of those brilliant scientists who prefer to work behind the scenes, without any clamor of publicity. He has a B.Sc. degree from the University of California, at Los Angeles, and a Ph.D. degree from the same university, at Berkeley, where he majored in biochemistry. For three years thereafter he was a Lilly Postdoctoral Fellow at Cornell University Medical College, New York City. While there, in collaboration with Dr. Vincent du Vigneaud, Nobel Prizewinner in chemistry, he synthesized vasopressin, one of the hormones of the pituitary gland. Thereafter he joined the research staff of the Virus Laboratory of the University of California, at Berkeley, and in collaboration with Dr. Wendell Stanley, Nobel Prizewinner in medicine, he elucidated the chemical structure of the protein of tobacco mosaic virus. In 1960 he joined the research staff of the Upjohn Company, a pharmaceutical establishment, in Kalamazoo, Michigan, where he is specially interested in the synthesis of biologically active compounds related to medical science. Dr. Gish is very active in Christian work.

NATURAL human life resides, basically, in cells. That is true of all living organisms, but we are dealing with human beings in this chapter.

Present-day scientists who attempt to create life in a test

tube know that their best chance to do so, if at all, is by duplicating or imitating the variety of material in the living cell and by manipulating this material with exact precision. These attempts, because of their exciting nature and novelty and on occasion because of the big names connected with them, have received much publicity of late and have set many people wondering. Things have been carried so far that only a few months ago, at this writing, Dr. Charles C. Price of the University of Pennsylvania, the president of the American Chemical Society, publicly urged that the United States make creation of life in the laboratory a national goal —at least, so one of the largest publications in the country reported. It was not stated whether this would mean another dip into the tax-money bucket.

Seriously, what about these attempts? Let us see.

The living cell is one of God's most marvelous creations. The complexity of its structure and of its many metabolic pathways is almost beyond comprehension. Consider alone the membrane that surrounds the microscopic object. This membrane is not merely a means to hold the contents together. It is not passive in its function, but active—in fact, dynamically active. Hundreds of research scientists have studied the cell membrane for many years, and today we are only *beginning* to gain an insight into its structure and function. We have found that it is complex, that it does not function as a simple sieve but utilizes complex mechanisms to admit or exclude various molecules. The nature of these mechanisms is still unknown. It is one of our many problems.

The membrane is only one of many complex structures that make up the living cell. The mitochondria, site of the many complex enzymes and other molecules that generate energy for the cell; the microsomes, site of protein synthesis (combination); and the nucleus, site of the functioning and reproduction of the genes (carriers of heredity), are examples of some of the structures or organized elements found in the living cell. All these elements and many others must be *organized*—and in a very precise way.

Cells are sensitive, extremely so. It has been shown that when cells are subjected to sonication (bombardment with high-energy sound waves) at certain energy levels, they cease to synthesize (unite) protein and nucleic acid, although they remain intact and normal in appearance. After sonication ceases, they resume synthesis. They won't stand for any interference or annoyance, however slight.

The living cell contains many types of molecules (microscopic particles). In order to get some idea of the complex mechanism required to synthesize one single type of molecule, let us say a few things about the *protein* molecule. Let us note:

1. Protein molecules are an absolute must for the life of the cell.

2. The enzymes, which are required to catalyze (accelerate) almost every chemical reaction in the cell, include protein as part or all of their structure.

3. A great many structural molecules are proteins, and many of the hormones (excitative secretions) are also proteins.

4. Proteins are complex polymers—that is, compounds of two or more molecules *of the same kind.*

5. The building blocks of proteins are amino acids, about twenty different kinds of which are found in proteins.

6. The proteins vary in size from those which contain about fifty amino acids to those which have several hundred.

7. Not only is the nature of the structure and biological activity of a protein greatly affected by the number and kinds of amino acids it contains, but also the *sequence* of the amino acids in the protein chain is of critical importance.

To get an idea of the size of a protein molecule, note that it takes an aggregate of several hundreds of them to make them visible under an ordinary high-powered microscope.

The information about a protein molecule just given is of a general introductory kind and has said nothing about the extremely complex mechanism necessary for the synthesizing (combining, completing) of just one of such molecules. The complexity of this mechanism is of such a nature that we cannot possibly go into it in the present chapter. It involves too many technical details—chemical and biological processes that are usually indicated by a great variety of laboratory diagrams, figures, and numbers.

There are three peculiarities of the cell in general, however, that should be mentioned:

First, our technical studies of the cell have much to do with the genes, which are composed of deoxyribonucleic acid (DNA). The number of the genes in one microscopic human cell is immense: between 20,000 and 30,000. The gene is believed to contain all or most of the information required by the cell to synthesize a particular protein molecule, such as that which we have been discussing. Structural genes are segments of a chromosome, and they are located in the nucleus of the cell. The protein molecule is synthesized, not in the nucleus, but in the microsome, located outside the nucleus in the cytoplasm of the cell.

How is the information for the synthesis of a particular protein molecule carried from its structural gene to the microsome, the site of synthesis? It is believed that there exists some sort of messenger composed of ribonucleic acid (RNA), and it has been designated messenger RNA. Just as there is a structural gene for each protein, so there is a corresponding messenger RNA for each protein. The way in which the messenger finds the protein, outside the nucleus, and conveys its message is very interesting but too intricate for further dilation.

In the second place, another important factor in the synthesis of a protein molecule is the energy required to bring about the formation of chemical bonds (substances that bind together). This necessary energy must be delivered in just the right form in order to be utilized. The energy is furnished in the form of high-energy chemical bonds found in certain kinds of high-energy compounds. These high-energy compounds are synthesized in the mitochondria (see the

[40

beginning of the chapter), where there is found a series of enzymes which are capable of breaking down chemical compounds, such as sugar, and converting the energy thus released into high-energy chemical bonds. The compounds containing these bonds are a necessary and vital part of our protein-synthesizing system, for without energy synthesis could not proceed.

The great complexity of the energy-producing system in the mitochondria can be imagined when it is realized that to oxidize (turn by adding oxygen) a molecule of a simple sugar, such as glucose, to carbon dioxide and water, at least twenty chemical steps are required, each of them catalyzed (accelerated) by a different enzyme (fermentative substance). For the oxidation of other kinds of sugars and other types of molecules—such as fats and alcohols—other series of enzymes, equally complex, are required.

In the third place, the control mechanisms at work in a living cell are absolutely essential to its survival. Every one of the many thousands of metabolic pathways (pathways for chemical change) in the cell is under close control at all times. The control mechanisms at work in the cell originate on the gene level. We have discussed the structural gene that carries the information for the synthesis of protein. What activates the structural gene when there is need for the protein for which it codes (prepares messages)? What shuts it off when sufficient protein has been synthesized? Evidence is accumulating that in addition to structural genes, the chromosomes contain genes whose sole function is to control the activity of the structural genes. The bacterial chromosome has been shown to contain regions whose sole function is to switch on and off the executive action of other regions; in turn, these *operator* genes are controlled by *regulator* genes. The presence of such control mechanisms converts what might be purposeless or even self-destructive activity into the ordered system we find in every living cell.

Every thinking person, of course, stands amazed at the intricacies and complexities of the—to the naked eye—invisible cell. At the same time he will not be surprised at all at the testimony of every honest scientist that although biochemical science has made great progress, there are a multitude of questions and problems remaining, both great and small. The greatest scientists, if they are frank and honest, will concede the greatest number of problems because they see and know more than the rest of us.

We have discussed, very briefly, the synthesis of a protein molecule. There is much about this that our best-qualified men do not yet understand. And the protein synthesis is but one example of the many highly complex syntheses performed by the cell. The syntheses of the various nucleic acid molecules and those of carbohydrates and lipids (fats) are equally complex. Even the synthesis of a relatively small and simple molecule, such as an amino acid, requires a whole series of chemical steps, each catalyzed (accelerated) by a different enzyme. Let us not forget also that each of the thousands of enzymes found in the living cell is in itself a highly complex molecule. And now certain men have undertaken to create life for us in a test tube!

The great question at this juncture is whether the men engaged in this heroic endeavor are thoroughly familiar with all the scientific details of cell life, whether they understand all the detailed workings, interrelationships, and influences of the myriad cell ingredients. Not one of them would assert that he does. Cell life is beset with problems. Yet the cell is the ultimate seat of life. As long as scientists don't know everything—literally everything—about life, isn't it rather thick and incautious to attempt a mechanistic production of it?

Of course, the scientists in question (and they are, in all seriousness, brilliant men) draw their courage for the attempt to create life from their hypothesis that life originally arose from inanimate or nonliving material, that the origin of life was due to a process caused only by physical and chemical laws that are in operation this very day, and that no intervention by an intelligent being, such as the biblical

Creator, was required. They speak of a chemical development, thereafter a biochemical development, and finally, after eons of time, the sudden appearance of the first living cell.

The readers must not expect me to enter into an argument with the proponents of this theory. I mean to write affirmatively and positively. As a scientist, I cannot and do not go along with these proponents. Also as a scientist, I can only see that the living cell, inconceivably complex, demands a Planner, that this tremendous *organization* requires an *Organizer*. The physical and chemical laws operating today, which must have been operative since the days of creation, are completely incapable of giving rise to the unique, specific, and purposeful structures and organization that we find in the living cell.

As for the great mystery of life, I simply and definitely accept the testimony of Genesis: "And the Lord God . . . breathed into man's nostrils the breath of life." (Gen. 2:7, AV) I accept Job's testimony: ". . . the breath of the Almighty hath given me life." (Job 33:4, AV) I accept the Apostle Paul's testimony: "He (God) giveth to all men life, and breath, and all things." (Acts 17:25, AV)

Life is more than just a master chemical, more than a vast collection of molecules endowed with special properties, more than the many hundreds of thousands of chemical reactions that occur in protoplasm. Life, as represented by the living cell, is a vast master plan, unique in this universe, incomprehensibly complex, awesomely constructed. Life was the climactic event in the creation of the universe by a Supreme Intelligence who declared, "For as the heavens are higher than the earth, so are my ways higher than your ways, and my thoughts than your thoughts." (Isa. 55:9, AV)

I share the conviction of a leading scientist, who declared, "Man will never create life until he knows everything about life, which means never."

"ONLY GOD CAN MAKE A TREE"

—Joyce Kilmer

BY LEONARD F. BURKART

WOOD CHEMIST and

TECHNOLOGIST

Dr. Burkart is a specialist in the biochemistry of wood, and he wrote of this fast-developing branch of science in a letter to the editor: "The more I delve into the fantastic complexity of wood, the more I am led to believe that there is a very wise and thoughtful Creator-God back of it all." He followed an extensive course in his specialty at the University of Washington and gained the degrees of B.F. and M.F., and he was thereafter graduated with M.Sc. and Ph.D. degrees from the University of Minnesota. He is currently a professor at the School of Forestry which is connected with the Stephen F. Austin State College, Nacogdoches, Texas.

AN expression that I frequently hear in scientific circles is "Mother Nature did thus and so" or, with a slightly different wording, "Nature has a way of taking care of such and such a situation." I once asked a prominent biochemist why he was willing to ascribe to nature a personality and an intelligence, rather than to say that God created or set the course of things in a particular way. He replied that it was acceptable in scientific parlance to refer to nature in this way, whereas reference to God would be construed as mixing science with religion.

So there was a frank confession of belief in modern dualism—spirit and matter, religion and natural science, God and His material creation, in two separate compartments, hermetically sealed. Either that, or our prominent scientist followed a certain very common type of frivolous reasoning: that the God of religion is really not wise enough or great enough to be the God of science also and that, therefore, no reference should be made to Him when one discusses matters of a purely scientific nature.

As a scientist, I acknowledge God, "in whom are hid all the treasures of wisdom and knowledge." (Col. 2:3, AV) I believe that in Him reside all the causative intelligence and energy that keep this fantastically complex, yet often amazingly simple physical and organic universe in its proper order.

I have some acquaintance, for example, with trees, those wonderful organisms that are so common that we barely notice them. They have no intelligence, as human beings have. But they do pass through infant, juvenile, and mature stages in their life-span, and barring disease or injury they eventually die of old age. It has been estimated that each cubic foot of a conifer tree (a tree that bears cones), such as a spruce, contains 10,000,000,000 to 14,000,000,000 cells. Each of these cells, while it is alive, is in a sense a tiny factory, which not only performs a particular function for the tree as a whole, but also manufactures the cellulose, hemicelluloses (part cellulose and less complex), and lignin (a relative of cellulose) that make up its own cell walls.

One of the most wonderful and truly mysterious happenings of nature or, as I prefer to put it, evidences of the reality of an intelligent Creator, is the ability of living cells to subdivide and to produce other living cells. In trees this subdivision is initiated primarily in a single-layered sheath of cells in what we call the cambial zone, between the woody

45]

tissue (xylem) and the bark tissue (phloem). These cambial or initial cells are responsible for producing all the secondary growth of the tree, which means the bulk of the tree in its full diameter. If the daughter cell, produced when the cambial or initial cell subdivides, is differentiated (marked for a particular function) toward the outside of the tree, bark tissue is formed. If the daughter cell bears certain other characteristics and is differentiated toward the inside of the tree, woody tissue is formed. Two distinct types of plant tissue are formed from the same single initial cell. How? How is that engineered? Nobody knows. Nobody except the Divine Engineer (I am speaking reverently) in Heaven. We are facing a great unsolved problem. And this cell action is repeated billions and trillions of times over, without a flaw.

We face still another mystery, of possibly still greater proportions. The ratio of cells for each tissue, wood and bark, is not one to one, as chance or probability would predict, but *several* to one in favor of woody tissue cells. Each one of the millions of cambial or initial cells that form the cambial sheath of the tree normally produces bark and wood cells in exactly the same ratio as *all the other* mother cells—the millions of them. In ordinary circumstances there is never a mix-up or a fault. What natural impulse or mechanism is responsible for this? What is the secret back of this astounding phenomenon, old as the ages and ever new? We don't know. It's a problem, apparently unsolvable.

There is more. There is, for example, a single woody tissue daughter cell from a typical porous tree (a tree that absorbs moisture). As it matures, it may increase in diameter several hundred percent and form a vessel segment whose chief function is conduction of water up the trunk or stem, or it may elongate several hundred percent and form a fiber whose chief function is mechanical support, or it may change very little in size to form a parenchyma cell whose chief function is storage of reserve foods. Again the ratio of these various types of cells is not what would be predicted by probability or chance but is such that a well-organized and highly functional tissue is produced. So the strange, varied, yet correct ratio of these cell types presents us with another problem —an amazing one. No one understands how the desired ratio, for the desired result, is obtained. It all speaks of an infinitely brilliant Designer—certainly not of capricious chance.

If the tree happens to be growing on a hillside or is permanently bent over by the wind or some other agency so that it is not growing in a vertical direction, there is produced abnormal tissue (reaction wood) that attempts to force the tree trunk into a vertical alignment and thus to keep the center of gravity of the tree in a relatively stable position. In conifer trees the reaction wood is located on the lower or compression side of the lean. This wood has a higher than normal lignin content, which increases the compressive strength of the lower side of the tree and tends to "push" the tree back into vertical alignment. In angiosperms, or broadleaf trees, on the other hand, the reaction wood is located on the upper or tension side of the lean. This wood has a higher than normal cellulose content, which increases the tensile strength of the upper side of the tree and tends to "pull" the tree back into vertical alignment. If the tree becomes realigned with the vertical, or nearly so, normal wood is again produced by the cambium.

How does one who is seeking logical scientific explanations of natural phenomena account for the contrary-to-the-laws-of-probability behavior of living, marvelously structured, yet in themselves unintelligent trees? What prompts the mother cell to produce the right kind of daughter cells in just the right ratio, or what prompts the daughter cell to mature into just the particular cell types needed, so that in the aggregate a wonderfully balanced organism is formed? We can shrug our shoulders or say that this is the result of enzyme and hormone activity which we don't as yet fully understand. But is that solving the problem or problems? Isn't it more reasonable and logical to look upward and confess that we have a God whose creative and sustaining wisdom and power know no bounds and that this is, as yet, one of His great mysteries?

As for plant enzymes and hormones, the role of these cell secretions in biochemical activity, growth, and reproduction, is a large and fascinating subject. These complex substances often display an apparent intelligence that science is just beginning to probe and examine. There is, for instance, the reawakening of perennial plants after a dormancy period during the winter months. A combination of temperature and photoperiod (the relative lengths of light and darkness as they affect the growth and maturity of an organism) evidently is responsible for triggering renewed growth activity in the spring. If either the temperature or the photoperiod is not right, photosensitive plants will remain dormant and are not fooled by any unseasonably warm spell that may be passing through. The plant hormones, or auxins, that are the activating agency for renewed growth activity require stimulation by both light and temperature conditions, and they in turn stimulate the different ratios of the plant's nutrient levels, which result in cambial activity and the production of foliage, flowers, and fruit.

The biochemistry of photosynthesis (union of chemical compounds by the aid of radiant light energy), in which even the simplest single-celled green plants are able to participate, is another of the wonderful happenings of nature that speak so eloquently of a supreme intelligence. Yet photosynthesis is merely the beginning of a fantastic series of processes that transform carbon dioxide, water, and a few other essential elements into living plant tissue and provide the energy necessary for the vital processes and activities incidental to life.

The very first verse in the Bible states: "In the beginning God created. . . ." Elsewhere the same Bible states: "Ever since the creation of the world his (God's) invisible nature, namely, his eternal power and Deity, has been clearly perceived (set forth) in the things that have been made." (Rom. 1:20, RSV)

I have the strange conviction that one reason many people would rather have faith in nature and mutation than in God is that to admit the existence of a living and intelligent God implies a dependence on Him and a personal responsibility to Him. Faith in nature which we supposedly can see and, to a limited extent, manipulate is to them scientifically acceptable, whereas faith in a personal God who created all things is considered naïve.

That science has made tremendous strides, especially in the last 50 to 100 years, toward understanding the "how" of many natural phenomena is unquestionably true, and as our scientific knowledge increases many more secrets of nature will undoubtedly be discovered. Science has made much less progress in the fields of "why" and "for what purpose," in regard to these same natural phenomena.

Personally I find no difficulty in believing that "behind the dim unknown" of scientific endeavor and achievement there is a God who keeps everything in its proper order. My own life and attitude toward science have taken on new meaning since I have come to recognize and acknowledge God as the supreme motive and goal of life.

If there is a God, He must by definition be the God of science, as well as the God of theology, and any seeming contradictions between science and theology are no doubt due to man's incomplete knowledge of one or both of these subjects.

AGING, DREAMING, ETC.–NEWLY DEVELOPING SUBJECTS

BY A. KURT WEISS

PHYSIOLOGIST

Dr. Weiss is a physiologist of distinction. He is an Austrian by birth, and in 1940 he came to the United States, continued his education, became an American citizen, and joined the American Army to fight Hitler's troops in Europe. After his return here he acquired a B.Sc. degree from Oklahoma Baptist University, an M.Sc. from the University of Tennessee, and a Ph.D. in physiology from the University of Rochester. He held teaching posts at the University of Miami and Oklahoma City University, was an investigator at the Howard Hughes Medical Institute, and presently is a professor of physiology at the University of Oklahoma. Among the scientific societies of which he is a member are the American Physiological Society, the Endocrine Society, the Gerontological Society, and the Society for Experimental Biology and Medicine. His research work has led to many important scientific discoveries and an enviable reputation among colleagues throughout the land.

Note by the Editor

Dr. Weiss devotes a large part of his chapter to the subject of aging; Dr. Baker, following directly, devotes his entire chapter to the same subject. At first we were inclined to ask one of the learned gentlemen to choose another subject, to avoid duplication. But the subject matter is of such profound practical interest to every one of us living human beings and the approach of the two writers, we felt, would be so different that we decided to leave matters alone and quietly to proceed with this most impressive, deeply personal theme.

I have just finished browsing through a book entitled *A Treatise on Human Physiology Designed for the Use of Students and Practitioners of Medicine*. Its author, Dr. John C. Dalton, was a professor of physiology and hygiene in the College of Physicians and Surgeons in New York, and the seventh edition of the book before me was published in 1882. I have also just finished teaching the section on endocrinology (the science of glands and internal secretions) in a physiology course for medical students. Little of what is contained in Dr. Dalton's book is being taught today. Some of the material it contains is already known to our present-day science-minded high school youngsters; other material is obsolete and no longer regarded either as true or as important; conversely, the bulk of the material taught today was not even known in Dr. Dalton's day, less than 100 years ago.

Endocrinology is one such field that was completely unknown in 1882, and the word "hormone" was not yet coined. Many of the quantitative (dealing with quantity, amount, or extent) concepts of present-day physiology were also unknown then. The analysis of blood for respiratory gases had not yet been developed, and the clearance methods for studying kidney function were as unknown as was kidney function itself. The highly specialized field of physiological chemistry, which occupies a great deal of the medical student's attention during his first year in medical school, was not taught in a separate department, as it is today, and is covered rather quickly in about 100 pages of Dr. Dalton's book.

No scientist in his right mind would venture to predict the status of science even ten years from now. I am even wondering just which of the many seemingly fundamental and highly important concepts that are taught today will have been proved to be inaccurate, unnecessary, and obsolete, or will have been forgotten in just another few years. Surely, other topics and concepts not even conceived yet by the human mind will fill some pages of the textbook of physiology of the future, and functions only barely comprehended today may well have whole chapters devoted to them and whole monographs written about them.

Such functions as aging and dreaming were not mentioned in Dr. Dalton's book. Nor do a number of contemporary textbooks dealing with physiology make mention of these topics. Some of the most recent ones, however, do refer to these functions in a brief statement, and it is reasonable to assume that as an increasing amount of data is gathered, increasing attention will be given to these bodily functions.

Thoughts on Aging

The noted British gerontologist (specialist in aging) Dr. Alex Comfort recently observed that serious research into the control of age processes has now moved out of the "field of eccentricity" and is gradually becoming a subject of scientific research by standard methods.

All of us age, and probably all aspects of an individual are involved in the aging process. Not all of us achieve old age, nor do all of us possess tissues and organs that are already demonstrating the gross changes of senescence (process of aging) or that will be capable of living long enough to acquire the characteristics of old age. Barring accidental death, why do some individuals acquire the characteristics of old age and then continue to live for a long period of time, while others have tissues and organs that apparently break down and cause life itself to cease? Today the answers to these questions are not known, and scientists are only slowly beginning to understand what constitutes the changes of progressive aging at the organ, tissue, and cellular levels. This is, as of now, one of our great unsolved problems.

There is really a dual problem with which the worker in this field is confronted. The first is to understand the alterations in the body that are caused by the aging process itself. It is rarely, if ever, true, however, that an individual ages without *at the same time* acquiring other debilities that may or may not bear a direct relationship to the aging process. The second problem, consequently, is concerned with the very complex and difficult task of isolating the effects of aging from the other effects and of assessing if these two simultaneously progressing events are related to each other. This sort of analysis is still in a stage of infancy. Yet in the last few years an increasing number of scientists have interested themselves in these processes. While today it may even be difficult on occasion to ask intelligent questions in this area of human interest, there may be forthcoming, in the not too distant future, answers that will help in gaining a better insight into the mechanisms of the aging phenomenon.

The early stage in which the study of aging finds itself at the present time is perhaps readily depicted by the curious situation that the people who do the research on aging cannot apparently agree on a definition of it. In a vague sense almost everybody has some idea of what is meant by the term "aging," but when a more precise statement about the meaning of this word is required things become difficult. The same difficulty is encountered when an attempt is made to specify the onset of the process. While some people contend that certain processes of aging begin in the as yet unborn embryo in the womb, others are inclined to feel that a certain degree of maturity must have been attained before aging can be said to have been initiated. Dr. John H. Heller, the executive director of the New England Institute for Medical Research, in Ridgefield, Connecticut, declared at a recent Conference on Dynamic Therapeutics in Geriatric Medicine held at St. Joseph's Manor, in Trumball, Connecticut:

> We suspect that aging is programmed in a genetic clock. By this I mean that every species we know anything about . . . has an average lifetime which varies enormously from one species to the next. It varies from a few hours, as in the case of the mayfly (*Ephemera*), to hundreds of years, in the case of certain tortoises. These life spans seem fixed; it is as though there were a genetic clock which at time X, more or less, turned itself off, and that is that. . . . This clock isn't turned off simply because there's gradual decay, or deterioration, or an accumulation of degenerative diseases, because there are various species where these things do not happen. The organism just stops living. You can do the most elaborate pathology, and there is no apparent cause of death. (Quoted from the medical trade journal *Geriatric Focus*, Vol. 4, No. 10 (1965), pp. 1-2, with the permission of the publishers, Knoll Pharmaceutical Company, Orange, New Jersey.)

If one were to agree that all of us possess such a clock mechanism, which slowly but surely advances our bodies to an older state with passing time, then invariably the questions arise: But what triggers this clock mechanism to advance, and what specific tissue-related alterations, called aging, does the mere passing of time produce in the organism? Obviously, no single cause or trigger or multiple causes have been isolated.

A number of ideas have been advanced, however, attempting to explain, at least in part, how and where the changes accumulating with the passing of time are made to impinge on the body. There is the accumulation of metabolic products theory. The accumulation of deleterious (injurious) products of metabolism (chemical changes in cells) has been proposed as one theory which may explain some of the alterations in the organism with the passing of time. Is this accumulation a cause or an effect of aging? If one regards the inherent clock mechanism as the causative factor, then the metabolic accumulation may well be the product of it. An example may illustrate this concept. When one studies a specific muscle—say, the triceps muscle of the right arm—he will find that the number of fibers making up this muscle does not increase during the lifetime of the individual. Although an individual fiber can be strengthened and made to increase in diameter, the total number of fibers will not become greater during the individual's life-span. In middle life and thereafter, however, some of the individual fibers may degenerate, and the triceps muscle will weaken. The space previously occupied by some of the actively contracting muscle fibers is now occupied by a new material, the connective tissue. Its volume is similar to that of the muscle fibers which were previously there; but the connective tissue has no contractile ability, and its contribution to the overall metabolism of the muscle is quite insignificant. The muscle in which these accumulations of connective tissue have occurred is weak, and this condition is one that is often encountered in old age.

Then there is the wear and tear theory. The wearing out of certain materials in the organism has been proposed by others as a theory of aging. From an anatomical point of view the wearing out of the triceps muscle which has just been described may serve as one illustration of this idea. Even if there is no immediately detectable deterioration at the gross anatomical level, certain ultrastructural components of the cell and their biochemical constituents may have begun to function less efficiently because of the wear and tear experienced by them. Enzymes are biochemical catalysts (accelerators), which are composed primarily of protein. Since most functional processes are regulated by some enzymatic activity, it is not difficult to conceive of a situation where a breakdown has occurred at the enzymatic level of a tissue or cell. This breakdown may have more than just a local effect on the organism, since the breakdown of

55]

even a relatively simple enzyme complex is known to have far-reaching consequences in the behavioral and functional activities of the organism.

Finally, there is the mutation theory. This theory of aging is an intriguing one. From a genetic viewpoint (point of origin) all processes and functions of life are controlled by the chromosomes in the nucleus of the body cells. Man is believed to have forty-six such chromosomes in most cells. Situated at a definite location on a particular chromosome in each cell nucleus is the gene, a factor which controls one specific entity (body substance). Occasionally, in fact extremely rarely, an error occurs in the chromatin material which makes up the chromosome, thus producing a defect at some specific site on the chromosome in a body cell. This defect is known as a mutation (alteration) and may have far-reaching consequences in the entity which the affected gene controls.

Although it is believed that in nature mutations occur spontaneously, they can be induced experimentally by exposure of the organism to a variety of influences which increase the mutation frequency. X rays or other ionizing radiation are known to exert such an influence, as do other events, such as exposure to ultraviolet light, heat, and certain chemicals. The longer an organism lives, the greater are its chances to acquire mutations because of the lapse of a greater time span. Some scientists feel that it is the acquisition of such mutations in the genetic makeup of the individual which underlies the processes of aging and hastens the onset of death. Experimental work on laboratory animals has shown that exposure to ionizing radiation accelerates the onset of certain phenomena that are related to aging and thus shortens the life-span.

The acquisition of a mutation in a reproductive cell may be transmitted to the offspring. When mutations are acquired later in life and the organism is no longer engaged in procreative activities, such transmissions are, of course, no longer possible.

The ideas just presented are theories—that is, they are intriguing suggestions of how aging may come about, but they are not necessarily the conclusive facts which have been proved to be the actual causes of aging. Perhaps other phenomena, not even thought of as yet, may ultimately prove to be the factors that cause aging in the organism.

The maximum life-span of man has not been significantly altered since biblical times. Atmospheric contamination may well bring on a shortened life-span for man in the future, but for the present the prevention and cure of certain disease processes, which in the past have taken a relatively early toll of life, have enabled a fairly large percentage of the world's population to have a life-span closer to the maximum.

The reference to biblical times reminds one of man's dual nature: that he is both a physical and a spiritual being, that he has both a body and a soul. In connection with our present theme we are perhaps thinking of the prayer of Moses, the man of God: "So teach us to number our days that we may apply our hearts unto wisdom." (Ps. 90:12, AV) To number our days means to think seriously about our process of aging. That in turn may make us think of the beginning of man's history—the Garden of Eden and the tree of life, whose fruit, after man's transgression, he might not eat and thus live forever (Gen. 3:22-24, AV). But Christ, the second Adam, in His saving mercy made another tree of life possible: "To him that overcometh will I give to eat of the tree of life. . . ." (Rev. 2:7, AV) There are no unsolved problems about *that*.

New Ideas About Dreaming

There are many other subjects, besides aging, under the head of natural science that in late years have seen fresh development and new interpretations. Let us mention just one more subject—that of dreaming. I am choosing this particular subject, not only because it is familiar to everybody, but also because people usually do much wondering about it and because it frequently leads to misunderstandings and, occasionally, emotional disturbances.

What is the newest and latest information about our dream life? Are any problems in this field still remaining?

Around the turn of this century Sigmund Freud, the Viennese physician, probed the world of dreams. In the book *The Interpretation of Dreams*, published in 1900, he suggested that dreams are the fulfillment of wishes and that the occurrence of dreams acts as a safeguard to sleep. To him, many types of mental illness appeared to be similar to dream life, and it occurred to him that by probing into the dreamworld of an individual he might gain access to the regions of the unconscious which might conceivably be responsible for the mental ailments with which modern man is so often afflicted.

It was this concept that led Freud to develop the technique of psychoanalysis, which makes use of dream recollections and interpretation, a practice known in early Old Testament times. Briefly, the patient is encouraged to recollect one of his excursions into the dreamworld and to relate his reactions in great detail, but without further reflection. With the information thus gained, the psychoanalyst may uncover some of his patient's repressed wishes and, by helping him understand the significance and true nature of these repressed complexes, may lead him to a more acceptable behavior pattern.

This Freudian theory has completely dominated the understanding of the phenomenon called dreaming during the first half of the twentieth century. Only during the last ten to fifteen years have some new ideas been injected into this field. As a result of these new ideas some investigators of the dream phenomenon have shifted their focus from the realm of the mind and its *psychology*, which Freud stressed, to that of the brain as an organ and to its *physiology*.

Working in the Sleep Laboratory of the University of Chicago, Dr. N. Kleitman and collaborators made the observation that the sudden bursts of rapid and jerky eye movements which they recorded in sleeping subjects could be correlated with a dream experience by the subjects. This discovery made possible scientific measurements of dreams. By connecting electrodes from the temples of the subject's head to a brain wave detection apparatus (electroencephalograph), it became possible to record the brain wave activity of a sleeping subject and to correlate this with eye movements, heart rate, and respiratory rate. The periods of greatest activity of these measured functions show up simultaneously during sleep.

Furthermore, when individual subjects are awakened after a distinct and specific brain wave pattern has appeared on the recording device, they are almost always able to recall the contents of their dream. It appears that the rapid eye movements in the sleeping subject are indicators of visual events which the dreamer experiences and that the dreamer participates in the dream with both emotional and physiological responses, as if it were an experience during the waking hours of the day. The dreamer thus observes or engages in a continuing, ongoing situation, as in real life. Certain sequences may be shortened, others may be left out entirely, but the action continues and appears to occupy more than just a fleeting moment. Indeed, there is some evidence which suggests that an episode in a dream takes as long as it does in real life.

It may surprise many of us to be informed that the average adult dreams four dreams a night and that each one is longer than the previous one. They usually last from a few minutes to an hour or more. We don't, of course, remember them all and oftentimes forget them entirely.

In spite of certain similarities to real life, the dream state has unique physiological characteristics that differ from those of the awake state and of dreamless sleep. This physiological state is centered in the nerve cells and is already present in newborn infants. The dream mechanism is therefore inborn. Apparently this mechanism is an essential one to the well-being of the individual. In a certain experiment sleeping subjects had their dream state disrupted by being awakened as soon as a dream brain wave pattern was noticed on the recording apparatus. They were then allowed to return to sleep and usually slept as much as other subjects who were not awakened. The dream-deprived individuals, however, became irritable and were easily upset during their waking hours. The experiment demonstrated that dreams contribute to our disposition while we are awake.

But there are unsolved problems. One of them is the mechanism that brings on the dream state. We don't know what it is. Another is the factors that are involved in dreaming. We don't know what they are. There are questions of greater detail that have not been answered. Experiments are currently under way in a number of laboratories, and scientists are trying to shed more light on the mysteries of dreaming that are still hidden from them.

The scientist who spends his working hours in the laboratory or clinic studying the functions and observing the marvelously intricate, yet so well coordinated, mechanism of the human body is a very fortunate person, for he gets an unparalleled opportunity to behold one of God's greatest creations—man. He cannot help being greatly impressed with and deeply moved by the creative genius of God, and he realizes evermore that: "The Lord God of gods, the Lord God of gods, he knoweth (has knowledge). . . ." (Josh. 22:22, AV)

It was this same Divine knowledge that made the Apostle Paul exclaim: "O the depth of the riches both of the wisdom and knowledge of God . . . !" (Rom. 11:33 and following verses, AV) Paul could find no adequate descriptive words for this knowledge, but it did make him break forth into an incomparable doxology.

PROBLEMS ENCOUNTERED IN THE STUDY OF AGING

BY DONALD G. BAKER

PHYSIOLOGIST

RADIOBIOLOGIST

After having graduated from the University of Toronto, Canada, with a B.A. in biochemistry and an M.A. and a Ph.D. in physiology, Dr. Baker was for six years a research associate in the university's physiology and medical departments. Later he became a special lecturer in radiation biology at the School of Hygiene and a director of the Radiation Research Unit. He was a professor of physiology and medical research until 1964, when he became a radiobiologist at the Brookhaven National Laboratory, Associated Universities, Inc., on Long Island, New York. Dr. Baker is a member of the Radiation Research Society, Canadian Physiological Society, Royal Society of Medicine (England), New York Academy of Sciences, and other organizations. He is the author of thirty published monographs, dealing with environmental stress and radiation injury. The present section of this symposium has been processed through the U.S. Security Office, in accordance with regulations.

AMONG the mistaken notions of modern life, indeed a cherished fiction of our North Atlantic culture, is the idea that modern science holds the key to a longer life-span than we have experienced up to the present. Already in the nineteenth century there were learned optimists who predicted that medicine would soon give us 150- or 200-year life-spans, and although the prediction did not come true, we again have many prophets among us who forecast the same marvelous happening, to come about in a very, very short time.

What about it? More than 3,000 years ago Moses wrote: "The days of our years are threescore years and ten (70 years); and if by reason of strength they be fourscore years (80 years), yet is their strength labor and sorrow; for it is soon cut off, and we fly away." (Ps. 90:10, AV)

How much have we improved on that, now, in the second half of the twentieth century A.D.? The answer is, not at all. Certainly not if we take the *average* life-span. And the average life-span for *all* modern humanity, including all the backward regions and countries, is considerably *lower* than the figure Moses noted down. Science has done a great deal —in the more advanced countries and while we of the present day are living our little life-spans—to prevent what are usually called premature or untimely deaths and to make life more bearable, but our life-span has remained pretty stationary. And there is little likelihood that medical science will be able to change the process of aging in the immediate future.

The reason for this rather sad situation is that the process of aging itself is little understood. I am persuaded that the most outstanding problem in the field of physiology is the mechanism of the aging process. This is a problem of infinite complexity. It concerns all living things, and while the process is universally recognized, even the gerontologists (specialists in aging) are unable to agree on a definition of aging.

Of the phenomena that are characteristic of advancing age in most organisms, few are more universal than the progressive inability to tolerate or adapt to environmental stress. Perhaps aging should be defined in these terms. Several theories have been advanced as mechanistic bases for senescence (aging), but they have for the most part dealt with

[62

broad and general principles, rather than with a comprehensive thesis embracing the numerous and diverse physiological functions which collectively characterize the aging process.

The ability to adapt to changes in environment is a universal characteristic of living organisms and is well recognized in human experience. There is an adage, however, which says, "You can't teach an old dog new tricks." While experience generally attests to the validity of this saying, the reasons for it remain to a large extent unknown. As for adaptation to environmental changes in animals at different ages, it has been observed that adaptation to low atmospheric pressure, to cold, and to heat occurs more readily in young animals than in the old. This was also true of such psychological tests as maze learning (when the animal's path was complicated by at least one blind alley). Young animals were able to remember the maze, even after four months. Older rats had much shorter memories, and some had no memory at all.

The basis for any of these responses has as yet eluded the physiologist, although it is generally assumed that changes in the central nervous system, progressing with age, are the critical factors. It should be pointed out, however, that at the present time there are few consistently observable age-dependent changes in the anatomy of the central nervous system. This is a great puzzle to the physiologists since this tissue is not renewed by cell proliferation, as is, for example, the skin or bone marrow. The effects of time might therefore be expected to produce more apparent, more visible changes.

But one must bear in mind that all adaptive phenomena (responses to environmental stress) are not affected by age. Hypertrophy (enlargement) of the heart, adrenals, and kidneys, when these organs are specifically stressed, seem to be independent of age. With advancing age, however, pathological changes (changes caused by disease) progress in these organs, making the interpretation of experiments difficult.

It is commonly recognized that all machines wear out or

deteriorate in time and that this is especially true of complex machines. Furthermore, those of us who must use apparatus that has interdependent parts and functions realize that even small decrements (losses or diminutions) of performance in individual components can greatly reduce the efficiency of the entire machine. By analogy, the wear and tear theory of aging has been applied to the human organism. On this basis it has been assumed that each organism is endowed with a limited physiological capacity, and when this reserve is depleted to a critical point, homeostasis (equilibrium or harmonious action) fails, and a progressive disorganization of interacting metabolic systems ensues, terminating in death.

This concept seems to be supported by Dr. H. B. Jones, who has made an extensive analysis of vital statistics from various populations of the world. He finds, as is well known, that the average life-span is increasing in many lagging countries as modern sanitation, better diets, and medical care are introduced. From a study of the statistics he concludes that as the health of any population improves, all diseases, not only the communicable diseases, are reduced about equally. He reasons that the general vitality of a population results in a decreased mortality for all diseases. Populations with a high incidence of disease in the younger age groups have a decreased resistance to disease in the older groups. It is as if one disease predisposed an individual to another disease later. This leads directly to the idea that senescence (aging) is caused by the summation of the insults which the individual receives.

Although this explanation of the aging process presents many interesting thoughts, the extensive and carefully controlled laboratory experiments by other scientists indicate that stress per se is not the essential factor in the aging process. However, it may play some role.

For some years geneticists have recognized that the offspring of older parents have a higher incidence of genetically determined defects than those from younger parents. It is generally assumed that the genetic constitution of an individual to a large measure determines both the rate of aging and the maximum life-span. Experts have pointed out that the somatic (body) cells of an animal should be just as subject to mutation as germ cells, and since practically all mutations are deleterious (injurious), the body cells would become increasingly inefficient as they developed these mutations. The organs of which they are a part would likewise become inefficient and, therefore, increasingly unable to withstand disease or other forms of stress. Subsequently, these scientists have amassed a significant array of experimental evidence that damage to the genetic elements of body cells increases with time. Using ionizing (converting into electrified particles) radiations as potent mutagenic agents, these scientists have shown the similarity between chronologically old animals and animals surviving a dose of radiation sufficient to have significantly increased the proportion of body cells that have chromosome abnormalities.

Similarities between the normal aging process and the changes following exposure to ionizing radiation were recognized more than a quarter of a century ago, when it was noted that the death rate among irradiated rats had significantly increased—a fact which mortality data have repeatedly confirmed. It is known that irradiation will increase the incidence of certain specific diseases such as neoplasms (tumors). But even if it is more a trend than a rule, the reduction in life expectancy following exposure is not always attributable to any specific disease but is associated generally with premature development of diseases associated with increasing age and to such an extent as to suggest a common mechanism.

The similarities between chronological aging and irradiation-accelerated aging in terms of mortality and disease incidence have counterparts at the physiological level. For example, it has become well established that younger or non-irradiated animals can adapt to environmental stress much better than older or irradiated animals.

At the present time it is not known to what extent the aging phenomena and the late effects of irradiation are the result of a common mechanism. Indeed, it seems that even in the face of the tremendous research efforts now in progress our success in acquiring an understanding of the aging process is far from assured. Besides the theories and assumptions about aging already mentioned, there are several others, some of which are referred to in a sentence or two.

During the past decade J. Bjorkstein has strongly supported the thesis that the aging process is closely related to the accumulation of protein fractions in body tissues—protein fractions that cannot be used for ordinary metabolic (chemically changing, energy-producing) purposes because of cross-linking. The presence of such proteins would weaken cellular and tissue function, thus disturbing the physiological balance of the whole organism.

F. M. Sinex, in his extensive studies, also implicates cross-linking in the development of senescence (aging). He calls attention to the possibility that the same cross-linking mechanism may result in the elimination or modification of essential molecules. Such action or changes would certainly result, he thinks, in a progressive decrement (decrease) in cell function.

These considerations have much in common with the somatic (body) mutation theory of H. J. Curtis and others. Another prominent scientist, S. Oeriu, however, looks on the process of aging as resulting from the accumulation of disulfide (chemical compound) bonds or links, which do apparently increase with age in many tissues of the body. Cause and effect in these various theories are seldom clearly delineated, and much research remains to be done if any sort of causal relationship between these biochemical changes and the physiology of aging is to be established.

In aging animals one of the most consistently observed deleterious (detrimental) changes is the progressive thickening of the connective tissue barrier between the blood and the parenchymal (tissue) cells through which oxygen, carbon dioxide, nutrients, and wastes must pass to and fro in order to maintain the normal function of the tissue. The increase in mass of the connective tissue barrier leads to progressive decrement (decrease) in the functional capacity of the various organs. The ultimate cause of these changes remains obscure. Disorganization of genetic information, cross-linking of connective tissue proteins, and a host of other processes appear to be implicated, but for the moment the primary cause remains obscure.

In addition to the basic mechanism of the aging process, there are a host of other, very intricate problems connected with the physiology of aging. For example, one of the readily observable changes occurring in the cells of aging organisms is the accumulation of age pigment particles. These pigmented bodies may be found in a variety of nondividing cell types. Their role in the aging process and even their chemistry are largely unknown.

It is a common experience to observe young men who are "old," while chronologically older men may appear younger. The physiological expressions of age are related to time, but in a complex, rather than a simple, relationship. This presents a very serious problem. How should age be measured?

It is a fact that the mammalian life-span (the life-span of breast-fed creatures) is closely correlated to brain weight. The larger the brain weight, the longer the life-span. It should be pointed out in passing that in man at least brain weight and size decrease progressively with age. This suggests that perhaps the determining factor in the length of life is the *precision* of physiological regulation. Such a thesis, however, is unlikely to be verified in the near future since we do not even understand the role of the central nervous system in homeostasis (equilibrium of body organs) or have the methods by which to quantitate (determine the extent of) this relationship.

Up to this point I have limited myself to brief comments about the physical, material aspects of aging as an important offshoot of the physiology subject. The reader will have noticed that physiologists know so much and understand so little. Again and again we run headlong into a variety of problems, unsolved problems. Many of these have been with us a long time—for centuries even—and there is no telling how many of them will eventually be solved.

It all stresses man's littleness, even when he has spent years of his life with books, in classrooms, and in laboratories. At the same time it emphasizes the infinite greatness of God and His works. It gives one a faint sense of the tremendous meaning of Jesus' words when in tones of holy conviction and warmest filial love He said, "My Father . . . is greater than all. . . ." (John 10:29, AV)

Both aging and death are a part of God's judgment upon transgression (Gen. 2:17, AV). I am told that the Hebrew language of this Scripture actually says, "Dying thou shalt die," meaning that physical death will usually be a *slow process* ending more or less suddenly. This is undoubtedly the spiritual source and background of the physical facts and problems that were under discussion.

But for myself, at least, there is yet another Scripture: ". . . I have the keys (the power) of hell and of death." (Rev. 1:18, AV) There is the music of life and of eternity in that!

PLANTS AND FLOWERS AND RHYTHMIC WONDERS

BY M. JOSEPH KLINGENSMITH

BOTANIST

Originally from North Dakota, Dr. Klingensmith spent the early part of his life close to nature, to plants and flowers, and one might call him a born botanist. He is a scholar of note in his specialty, and his formal education has been extensive. With a B.Sc. in botany from Wheaton College, he proceeded to Florida State University, where he gained the M.Sc. degree in microbiology and botany, and thereafter he acquired his Ph.D. in botany from the University of Michigan. He has held teaching positions at Ohio Wesleyan University and Colgate University, and he is presently on the faculty of Rochester Institute of Technology, New York. Professor Klingensmith is a member of the American Society of Plant Physiologists, Botanical Society of America, American Scientific Affiliation, and five other scientific bodies. His research specialty: plant growth regulators.

OUR Lord, when on earth, revealed himself as a great and enthusiastic lover of flowers. The one classic passage that shows this convincingly is found in the Sermon on the Mount: "Consider the lilies of the field, how they grow; they toil not, neither do they spin: and yet I say unto you that even Solomon in all his glory was not arrayed like one of these." (Matt. 6:28, 29, AV)

Some authorities think that in speaking of lilies the Lord had reference to the Huleh lily, a brilliant, often reddish-blue iris that still grows on the hills around Nazareth. Others think Jesus meant the red anemone, which is found abundantly in the valleys of Palestine in the springtime. But whichever flower Jesus had in mind, He knew flowers. He knew all vegetation better than any merely human being, including our modern master botanists, ever did, and He certainly had His reason for expressing himself as energetically as He did.

We are dealing with a highly important, marvelous subject—both plants and flowers. Let us enter this domain of God circumspectly and with a degree of awe.

With our reference to "modern master botanists" we did not mean to belittle the men referred to. Modern science—botanical science, too—has made tremendous headway in late years. Yet we are still at the beginning of the road—not in all, but in very many, respects. So let us proceed with the subject in hand.

At the present time we marvel at the wonders of modern chemical engineering. We can make simple molecules inexpensively in the factory, and we can string them together in regular fashion to form synthetic plastics and fibers, which are in such great demand. One doubts, however, if we shall ever be able to produce sugars, oils, proteins, and cellulose as smoothly, effortlessly, and inexpensively as the "lowly" plant does.

It is unfortunate that we have allowed the use of the term "plant nutrient" for the inorganic substances which the plant obtains from the soil and which we partially replace through the use of fertilizers. This term is misleading because it causes us to forget that the *basic* raw materials from which all plant parts are synthesized are carbon dioxide and water. Such synthesization is beyond human skill and endeavor. Imagine instructing a chemical engineer to produce the food and structural components of a plant, using the carbon dioxide available to him in the atmosphere at a concentration of 3 parts in 10,000 by volume, diluted with an excess of nitrogen and oxygen!

Perhaps it will be easier to understand the marvels of this feat if the figures are based on the acre unit. To grow a good field of corn which will yield 100 bushels, about 20,000 pounds of carbon dioxide are needed to provide about 5,500 pounds of carbon for the organic structures of the plant. This amount is about equivalent to the carbon contained in 4 tons of coal. No less than 21,000 tons of air must be processed by the acre of corn to recover and utilize this much carbon.

In addition to carbon, one of nature's major cycles is concerned with nitrogen, the key element in protein and other vital compounds. It is estimated that in the atmosphere above an acre of soil there are some 35,000 tons of free nitrogen. Yet although it is essential to life, not one molecule can be used directly by the higher plants, or by animals or man, without the intervention of nitrogen-fixing organisms (either saprophytic bacteria or the symbiotic legume—*Rhizobium* complex).

There are other sources of nitrogen. A little nitrogen is fixed by electric discharges in the air; much more of it, by the soil microorganisms. Man can bring about the fixation of nitrogen, but he requires a temperature of 500° C. and a pressure of hundreds of atmospheres. God's nature fixes more at ordinary soil temperatures and at ordinary atmospheric pressure than we can ever hope to do by one cunning process or another. Man faces a problem here that seems quite unsolvable. A well-nodulated (having small knots on the roots) *Rhizobium*-infected crop of alfalfa may produce on the average 200 pounds of fixed nitrogen per acre per season. In the form of commercial fertilizer this nitrogen would cost in the neighborhood of 400 dollars. Our farmers would hardly call that economical!

How many of us each winter look forward with anticipation to the coming of spring, with its spring flowers, and to the enjoyment of great varieties of beauty as they appear throughout the entire growing season! It was known from

71]

ancient times that various plants flowered at a particular season, but the reason for this occurrence was unknown. A part of this secret was unlocked for us by the work of Gardner and Allen, of the U.S. Department of Agriculture, who offered the effect of day length to explain flowering or floral induction in some plants, especially those known as short-day plants, or the common fall-blooming species (such as chrysanthemums), and as long-day plants, the common summer annuals of our gardens. They found that in almost every plant studied which has a long- or short-day requirement, it is the leaf which is the receptive organ to light control. This control for floral induction is transmitted from the leaf to the stem tip via some organic compound or compounds known as florigen, or flowering hormone.

Although the photochemical (light) receptor has been discovered and although the response to light stimulus varies according to the variety of plants, the challenging problem arises when one considers that it is the same compound (or physiologically similar compounds) that is responsible for the control of floral induction in both short-day and long-day plants. This has been demonstrated when two closely related plants requiring different light periods are grafted together and one receives the critical light period for its floral induction while the other plant is kept under conditions that would normally cause it to remain in a nonflowering or vegetative condition. Yet under these conditions both plants will flower, indicating that the control compound (or compounds) is transmitted by the graft and is effective in both plants.

It may be that in the future we shall be allowed to unravel some more of the mysteries regarding this process. But it causes one to think about the marvels of God's handiwork that allow a short-day plant, such as *Xanthium*, the common cocklebur, to distinguish between eight hours of darkness and nine hours of darkness. Under the latter condition it will flower, while under the former it remains in a passive, vegetative condition.

In addition to the timing of flowering, which is normally on an annual cycle, many plants have other timing systems built into them which continually challenge the botanist. For example, there are the diurnal (daily) rhythms in plants and animals. We are, of course, limiting ourselves to plants. During the 1700's and 1800's plant physiologists, such as Zinn (1759), Sachs (1857), and Pfeffer (1875), noticed that the orientation of plants in space was not constant but varied with the time of day. For example, the leaflets of *Oxalis* (wood sorrel) are spread at right angles to the sun during the day while at night they fold together like segments of a closed fan. These movements have been called sleep movements. Such a diurnal sleep movement occurs in a number of different plants, including many of the legumes (various clovers, alfalfa, soybeans).

The remarkable thing about the arrangement of the leaflets of *Oxalis* and other plants which exhibit this sleep movement is that the position of the leaflets is *not* the result of light falling on them. The movements continue on a cyclic basis of about twenty-four hours when the plants are transferred to either continuous darkness or light.

In addition to the opening or closing of leaves, other processes have been found to exhibit a diurnal rhythm. Secretion of perfume and nectar varies with the time of day in some flowers. This is especially true in many of the night-blooming flowers. The exudation of sap from the cut stump of the sunflower (*Helianthus*) exhibits a diurnal change in the rate of flow even when the plants have been previously exposed to a constant environment. Cell division in meristematic (embryonic) tissue which is undergoing rapid growth often exhibits maximum and minimum rates on a diurnal basis.

The biochemistry of the plant clock is unknown. It appears to run autonomously, without much reference to external environment, and is relatively insensitive to light intensity, to temperature, and to various metabolic (chemically changing, energy-producing) substances. In general, the phase and amplitude of diurnal rhythms are somewhat affected by the environment, but the basic period length can only be changed within narrow limits. An organism will adapt to an artificial rhythm of twenty or thirty hours from a normal twenty-four-hour rhythm but will either revert to its endogenous (produced from within) rhythm or exhibit highly disorganized activity when pushed beyond its limits. Light flashes, transitions from light to darkness, and abrupt temperature shocks can reset the phase or initiate the rhythms in the plants which are started under a continuous light or dark environment. It is clear, however, that these environmental aspects do not *cause* the rhythm. It seems to be genetically controlled. On the other hand, the cell mechanism seems to act without functioning of the cell nucleus, the master control center. It's one of our real unsolved problems.

Once we progress beyond the diurnal or annual rhythm in plants, the problem of the timing mechanism becomes still more, and much more, complex and baffling. For example, the periodicity of flowering in bamboos varies within wider limits than in any other homogenous (of like structure) group of plants. Some species flower annually, but other species have a far more prolonged life cycle and flower at intervals of twenty-five to thirty-five years. The great bamboo (*Bambusa arundinacea*) of India has a flowering interval of up to fifty years, although this seems to vary with the locality. The time cycle of flowering for *Bambusa polymorpha* of Burma exceeds eighty years.

In some bamboos both old and young shoots of the same clump, as well as cuttings from the parent clump, break into flowering simultaneously. This gregarious flowering occurs regardless of injury or even destruction of all portions above the ground by cutting or by fire. Even plants transported to different localities, including different continents, have been observed to burst into bloom at the same time as those that remained in their native habitat, making it seem unlikely that environment had any effect on this endogenous (produced from within) rhythm.

The completion of flowering usually is attended by the

production of seed, which provides for succeeding generations of plants. Although seeds have always roused man's curiosity, the complexity of the biological activity of seeds has not been widely appreciated. To the casual observer seeds appear to be dead entities, whereas in reality they are uniquely integrated living systems. But the fact that a seed is a living entity does not imply that it will germinate when placed in favorable environmental conditions. The process of germination requires a distinct quality in the seeds. A viable (living) seed may be incapable of germination because of some inherent deficiency, or it may be in a dormant condition—*i.e.*, a condition in which germination is temporarily delayed because of some action or inaction of the internal control mechanism. Germination of the seed follows the ability of the embryo to resume active growth after a period of inactivity.

Most seeds do not germinate immediately after ripening but have special mechanisms to delay germination until favorable conditions have arrived. This dormancy, or delayed germination, is particularly prevalent in the temperate regions where germination in the fall of the year would expose the seedlings to severe weather conditions.

But again we face unsolved problems. We do not know the *exact* causes and mechanisms of seed dormancy. The patterns of dormancy, however, suggest a very positive relationship between termination of dormancy and favorable environmental conditions. As such, dormancy is a time-measuring device. In this connection, *Xanthium* offers an interesting example. Its capsule contains two seeds which are differentially timed for germination by a year. In some oaks germination consists of two steps which occur a year apart. In the first year the root appears and grows; during the second year the epicotyl (upper portion) elongates with its leaves.

As stated, we do not know the control mechanisms that bring about this suspension of development and growth. The exact biochemical nature of the germination process remains obscure. More important, the biochemical patterns of the dormant seed during its inactivity are completely obscure. How is this prearrangement of a period of inactivity incorporated into the living system of the seed?

The complexities and problems dealt with above are, of course, only a few of very many. We may find some of the answers in the future. Experience, however, has taught scientists that as answers are found, new problems have a way of increasing and multiplying, making us ask, When is there an end? The answer to that is undoubtedly, Never, here and now. But for believers in God, I am sure, there comes a time when all mental fuzziness for us finite men will be cleared away. Bright sunshine will follow haze and mist.

In the meantime all men of faith will humbly and heartily assent to the words of the psalmist: "O Lord, how great are thy works! Thy thoughts are very deep." (Ps. 92:5, AV) Botanists, too, have discovered the truth of this ardent exclamation abundantly.

LITTLE SPACES CROWDED WITH
UNSOLVED PROBLEMS

BY PAUL G. BARTELS

PLANT PHYSIOLOGIST

Although Dr. Bartels has done the larger part of his re-search in plant cells and the great number of detailed scientific subjects connected with them, he is also well versed in related subjects and for that reason well qualified to enlighten us on botany in general. He was graduated from Concordia Teachers College, Seward, Nebraska, and thereafter acquired his B.A. and M.A. degrees from Colorado State College. Continuing his formal education, he received a Ph.D. from Vanderbilt University and then did postdoctoral research work at the University of California, at Davis. He taught biology at St. John's Junior College, Winfield, Kansas, and is presently a professor of botany at the University of Arizona. His specialties are organelle differentiation and chloroplast development.

THERE is a passage in the very beginning of the Bible that we usually read without much thinking, sort of glide over, as it were. It says that God himself brought the animals and the birds that He had created to Adam, to see what he would call them, "and whatsoever Adam called every living creature, that was the name thereof." (Gen. 2:19, AV) Adam at that time was still the perfect man, with a perfect mind and a perfect insight, and the names he gave to the various creatures reflected, were expressive of, their true nature and character. He also undoubtedly named them according to their species, genera, and structural and biologic relationship. In those very ancient, antediluvian days names, especially those of living beings, had a definite meaning and purpose. We see this continued, in some measure, in later Old and New Testament days.

What Adam did in the days of his pristine righteousness, our modern scientists seek to do in today's plant world. We call such scientists taxonomists, which means classifiers. They seek to classify plants into their proper groups and categories. (The same holds true of animal classifiers.) The trouble, of course, is that our modern men don't have the advantages of sinlessness and perfection, also of perfect intellectual acumen and discernment, and they find themselves running into many snags. What they want is not to categorize plants into arbitrary groups, but into groups that have genuine natural relationships. This is difficult.

For the general reader, animals would perhaps illustrate this difficulty better than plants. Many people would no doubt assume that all animals that live in the water form one large coherent group, or they would say that fish are animals that live in the water and have tails and flippers, and that this makes them logically and naturally a group with common characteristics. But whales and porpoises are not true fish but mammals—that is, members of a group related to dogs and cats. Applying this to the plant world, one can readily see that mistakes can be very easily made and that certainly arbitrary rules of classification are not always the best to categorize groups of organisms, animal or plant.

Scientists, in determining group relationships of plants, are oftentimes in the dark. They keep trying to find out such relationships in order to improve plant life, especially the plants that benefit man or provide pleasure for him. Practically all they can do along these lines is to interbreed—interbreed living plant groups to determine their various reproductive capabilities. Usually, only plants of the same natural group can interbreed successfully. With tens of thousands of plant varieties this requires diligent search. Taxonomists (classifiers) often speak of their problems!

In discussing the unsolved problems of botany, one should give special attention to the *seeds* of plants. Here again the Creator has demonstrated His greatness in the very small things of life. Everyone has observed that when a seed is planted in the soil and water is supplied, up shoots a young plant. There is no simple explanation of how an inactive or resting embryo of a seed is induced to grow into a plant. Various environmental factors, such as water, temperature, and kinds of light, have been studied to determine in what way these factors influence germination and growth of the embryo.

Some kinds of seeds, such as Grand Rapids lettuce seeds, will germinate well only when exposed to red light. If, however, after the red light exposure the seeds are then exposed to far-red light, they will not germinate. One can repeat the cycle of red—far-red light many times, and the last type of light which the seed "sees" or is exposed to will determine the outcome. If this last type is far-red, the seed will not germinate. This phenomenon is sometimes called the red—far-red light effect.

Scientists in government research laboratories in Maryland have been able to isolate a pigment, phytochrome, which absorbs red and far-red light and changes color with this treatment. Since lettuce seeds germinate in red light and are inhibited in far-red light and since the isolated pigment, phytochrome, changes from blue color to white under the same red light, researchers suggest that the two colors are related. When it is in certain forms (blue color), this phytochrome pigment induces the seeds to germinate.

The answer to the question of how phytochrome initiates this response in seeds is unknown. Many biologists have speculated on the exact mechanisms that enable a pigment to induce biological development. In fact, they wonder how any pigment can cause cells that are in an inactive state to divide and to result in new stems and leaves, especially since the pigment is on the seed coat and is not located near the embryo itself. This indicates that something is happening between the receptor pigment and the tissue which responds. Researchers are diligently working on this problem, but there has been no concrete evidence of a solution. We can say frankly that so far only God knows the answer.

Even more puzzling than the effect of light on seed germination is the manner in which water induces embryo cells to multiply and grow to seedlings. This very simple molecule of water causes the synthesis (combination) of new substances, such as proteins and lipids (fats), not found in the embryo but only present in the mature seedling and plant. Where do the new substances come from? I should make mention of the fact that the dry seed does contain an infinitesimally small amount of water. But this very minute quantity does not initiate a germinating response. An increased exposure of the seeds to water does the trick. But how? It is thought that the increased amount of water may dissolve some type of enzyme (accelerating substance) in the seeds and that the water provides a medium for the enzyme to act. But this is problematic. This is a theory, not an established fact.

Marcus and Feeley, in the government laboratory at Beltsville, Maryland, have come up with another explanation, but the nature of their work is too intricate and technical to allow detailed reporting or even summarization here. They have done exhaustive research work, and the explanation sounds plausible; but it is hardly definitive or conclusive. As of today, in this writer's opinion, the exact mechanism whereby water induces the synthesis and growth referred to above is still a mystery. It is still beyond man's comprehension—one of God's many, many secrets.

Naturally, there are any number of other problems connected with seeds and seedlings, especially in the line of growth regulators, or plant hormones. When one investigates a specific biological unknown, ten new mysteries pop up. It is a truism that research begets research, and we might add that problems beget problems, whether solved or not. I am afraid there will be no end to problems in God's great world. We are dealing with an infinite God, and there seems to be something of infinitude, of infinite depth and complexity, even in His material creation. Personally I cannot stop wondering at this faint semblance of infinitude when I look at the great sweep of the heavens above; I continue my wondering when I stoop down and examine the "little spaces" (see title of chapter).

There is photosynthesis. "Photo" means light; "synthesis" means a combination of parts, or a compound. Photosynthesis denotes a process, occurring in green tissue, in which energy from the sun is transformed into chemical energy, which in turn utilizes carbon dioxide to produce oxygen gas and complex sugars—glucose, sucrose, and other carbohydrates. This energy, derived from the sun, at the same time holds the atoms together in the sugar molecule.

Neither carbon dioxide nor water will burn (undergo combustion), nor would they make a very good meal. Carbohydrates (sugars, starches, cellulose), on the other hand, burn easily and release considerable energy in the process. When we eat the carbohydrates made by the plants, the energy in the sugars is converted to energy that is used in thinking, muscle movement, and other energy-requiring processes of the body. The great importance of photosynthesis lies in the transformation of low-energy compounds (carbon dioxide and water) into high-energy compounds (sugars).

Knowledge of photosynthesis is increasing as a result of the use of new techniques in research. But in spite of the very great amount of speculation and research that has taken place (ever since Aristotle observed that sunlight was needed for the greening of plants), photosynthesis still remains largely a mystery to scientists. In 1961 Melvin Calvin received the Nobel Prize for his research in photosynthesis, in which he discovered many reactions involved in carbon dioxide utilization. But after this tremendously important work scientists still ask, How do green plants trap light energy and use it to synthesize sugars from carbon dioxide and water?

Just as an organism grows slowly at first and then faster and faster, so scientific knowledge of a subject such as photosynthesis accumulates slowly at first; but as the background of information increases and is checked, verified, or discarded, the rate at which new knowledge is gained increases. Today our knowledge of photosynthesis increases fairly rapidly.

Even so, and with a large amount of photosynthetic research in progress, the mysteries of the subject are still very numerous. There still remain actually hundreds of aspects of photosynthesis that are unknown. We do not know exactly how light is absorbed by the chlorophyll in the chloroplast (the green coloring matter in its cellular mold or container) and how it is trapped as chemical energy. Many models have been used to explain how an electron is absorbed and energy trapped for later use. These models are derived from theories of physical concern with solid-state phenomena—all very involved, I grant! But such explanations are of a theoretical nature and may not be relevant to what goes on in the living plant. Research of this type is difficult to pursue, especially since biological systems are more complex than systems in the domain of physics. Many variables are inherent in a living system, while in nonliving systems only a few variables are present.

Another interesting problem involving various reactions of photosynthesis emerged a couple of years ago. There came to the notice of scientists a mysterious compound—a compound that would accept electrons from chlorophyll and hydrogen from the water in the cell. The hydrogen which was captured by this compound was eventually added to carbon dioxide from the air. At first this compound was identified with a multisyllable chemical, NAD. Further investigation showed that the scientists had been mistaken. It is now suggested that a hitherto undetected molecule is responsible for this newcomer to the company of compounds. There has been no identification of the stranger at this writing. How many other newcomers and strangers, we wonder, is our Creator keeping in "the dim unknown"? How many agents and forces, great or small, of whose existence we are entirely unaware, are there in nature? We don't know. Nobody knows.

For myself, let me say that I cannot imagine a world so full of mysteries and problems without a Creator-God. All I see is infinite wisdom and power—and finite men.

What we need is the true knowledge. Jesus one time said to an educated group of people, ". . . ye have taken away the key of knowledge. . . ." (Luke 11:52, AV) My dictionary tells me that one of the several meanings of the word "key" is "that which serves to reveal, discover, or solve something unknown or difficult." I am sure that one of the things Jesus had in mind was faith in God's creatorhood and unintermittent sustenance of that which He has created, from the onrushing star clusters above to the tiny particle in the microscopic plant cell.

IMPORTANT TO SEE BOTH
FORESTS AND TREES

BY LAURENCE C. WALKER

PLANT PHYSIOLOGIST
RESEARCH FORESTER

Dr. Walker is widely known as one of America's outstanding plant and tree specialists. His formal educational record in that line is impressive. With a B.Sc. from Pennsylvania State University he went to Yale, where he gained an M.F., and then proceeded to the State of New York College of Forestry, at Syracuse University, and earned a Ph.D. He was formerly a research forester in the U.S. Forest Service, and thereafter became a professor of silviculture, in charge of the Forest Physiology Laboratory at the University of Georgia School of Forestry. Presently he is the dean of the School of Forestry, Stephen F. Austin State College, Nacogdoches, Texas. Dr. Walker's specialties are forest soils, plant physiology, silvicides for hardwood control, and radioisotopology.

NATURALISTS are frequently guilty of not seeing the forests for the trees. That is, their concern for the identification and study of individual trees precludes the broader observation of the forest as an entity, if a complex one.

Ecology is the study of mutual relations between organisms and between them and their environment. The ecologist attempts to show the relationships of individual plants or

[84

trees to each other, to understand the interdependence of one upon the other in the biotic (life-sustaining) community, and, frequently, to utilize this knowledge for the improvement of man's already disturbed environment.

A literature review of a half century ago leaves the impression that at the time there were few ecologic questions left unanswered. More probably, it was the lack of qualified people to ask the questions or, perhaps, qualified writers among the people to voice the questions. Present-day students of nature formulate a dozen questions for each attempt to answer one of them.

A few such unanswered questions are discussed here. These are not theological questions. They do not ask if God is real, if He is creator and director. They simply indicate the belief of this Christian writer that in God's own time, with men of His own choosing, using minds and hands endowed by Him, these questions may be answered. It is not too much to anticipate many solutions in this generation as scientists (who, incidentally, may want no part of Him, yet may be used by Him) continue to examine the laws of nature.

The laws of nature we can ascertain. It is the laws of *human* nature that are so difficult to comprehend. Man, by his work, may search out the first. The second is revealed to the God-fearing person as he acknowledges dependence on the One of whom it is said to ". . . throw the whole weight of your anxieties upon Him, for you are His personal concern." (I Pet. 5:7, Phillips' translation)

Tolerance to Light and Water

The forester-ecologist recognizes various stages in the natural succession of a plant or animal community on any given site. For instance, in the New England States the colonists found a considerable area covered by spruce, fir, and hemlock forests. These are climax types—*i.e.*, if left alone, the species reproduce themselves under their own canopy indefinitely. Following clear-cutting or a devastating fire, however, spruces, firs, and hemlocks are not likely to reseed the area. Rather, white pine, fire cherry, or aspen enter as temporary or initial types. In time, perhaps 100 years later, spruce, fir, and hemlock will again dominate the site and remain dominant until this locale is again disturbed.

Why do some plants only inhabit open lands—the burned or clear-cut sites—while others insist on the shade of an overstory or the nurse tree effect of a single stem?

Pines generally require mineral seedbeds, free of humus, for seed germination, while the winged seeds of spruces and firs, not too unlike those of some pines, germinate in the litter of decaying leaves, needles, and twigs. Why?

After germination, whether in exposed mineral soil or in the organic duff, photosynthates (chemicals compounded through the agency of light) must be produced in the sprouts, and the functional capacity of the little sprouts or young shoots depends in considerable measure on the species of tree. Thus, shortleaf pines in their first two years form carbohydrate at about the same rate as shade-tolerant hardwoods of any age. But beyond that time the photosynthesis (compound-forming) rate in the pines diminishes appreciably. Hence, shortleaf and other southern pines entering an understory following a small fire—one that did not kill the overstory but did consume the litter on the forest floor to expose the mineral soil—frequently die in the third or fourth year for lack of adequate light. It is the red and blue quality in the spectrum which catalyzes (accelerates) the photosynthetic process. Not all species are equally efficient under equal illumination (lighting). In addition to the range of intensity, some respond more than others to certain light wavelengths.

But why this variation in tolerance to light? Was it arranged by the Creator, perhaps, to bring heterogeneity (diversity) to the landscape for the pleasure of man or to provide soil-saving cover for a variety of conditions? The answers to these and the preceding questions are, as yet, unknown.

Tolerance to water is a similar behavioral problem of plants that is not well understood. Bald cypress grows with its "feet" in the swamp; pond pine of the southeastern coast occurs in the pocosins (Indian for "swamps on a hill"); and sand pine, a closely related species, is found on the dry Florida sandhills. Although bald cypress and pond pine actually grow best on a mesic site—neither very wet nor very dry—competition on such sites is too great, so they are confined to the swamp, where few other species thrive to force their exclusion. On the other hand, the sand pines mentioned live under mesic conditions only when pampered!

A partial explanation of these phenomena is the reduction in water and salt absorption caused by deficient aeration (exposure to air) in flooded soil, the intake of which varies by species. But cell dehydration caused by decreasing water absorption (which ironically occurs with prolonged inundation) is not a reason for limiting growth. In fact and in contrast, wide and buttressed bases of trees are an indication of growth under this condition.

Chemical properties of poorly aerated soil, as a result of wetting, are important. Carbon dioxide is increased; nitrogen is bound to the organic matter; methane and complex aldehydes are produced; and toxic (poisonous) concentrations of ferrous iron, nitrites, and sulfides may accumulate. Yet each of these maladies can be corrected, and still intolerance to water is not overcome. Again the ingenuity of the Great Ecologic Manipulator has provided patterns for discussions which stimulate the mind of man. Problems are manifold, and they and their solutions have a way of begetting additional problems.

The Range of Species

The natural range of slash pine extends from the lower Florida peninsula northward into southern Georgia and westward to the Mississippi River. Growth for the species is probably best near the north-south center of the range—

87]

along the Florida-Georgia border. The species has been planted and successfully established north of its natural range and westward into Texas. Other plants, of course, have been introduced with phenomenal results across the oceans—for instance, our West Coast Douglas fir to western Europe, the Oriental honeysuckle and kudzu vines to the southeastern United States, and various eucalypti from the tropics to the subtropics. These are called naturalized if they maintain themselves in the new locale.

What factors control the range? Climate is one. Day length is another. White pine, for instance, grown in Florida from seed collected in the Great Lakes States is of poor vigor unless the day is artificially lengthened by stringing mazda lights over nursery beds. (This in turn affects the vigor of native trees in adjoining beds, making walls necessary to block out the light.)

Altitude affects the range, but not to the same extent as latitude, as is often thought. Latitude has a day-length effect, while altitude has probably more the effect of temperature and atmospheric pressure. How this last should influence the growth of vegetation has been theorized about, but it is not understood. (Lower partial pressures of carbon dioxide are found at higher elevations.) Nor do we comprehend physiological functions and other climatic criteria responsible for controlling the natural ranges of wild plants. There are many unanswered questions. Physiological ecologists keep seeking the answers, appreciating the hand of the Master Planner.

Branching Habit

The forester, in searching for super trees from which to collect seed for planting cutover land (land from which most or all marketable timber has been removed), looks for stems with a peculiar branching habit. Short slim branches which extend at right angles and prune naturally to leave small tight knots, are the ones desired.

In addition to inheritance, branching habit differs for

species and by environment. Spruces have a conical excurrent form (with undivided main trunk), while elms are known for a characteristic deliquescent (ramifying into divisions) vase-shaped crown. This is definitely inheritance. Environmental effect is illustrated by the tendency of open-grown trees to have bushy, widespreading crowns, while those in tight canopies generally are small and self-pruning. On the other hand, there are individual trees which, when grown in the open, have the kinds of branch expected from closely knitted forests, and vice versa. Part of this characteristic could be attributed to inheritance, but this has not yet been proved.

Research foresters test for genetic influences on branching by bagging male and female flowers of selected trees—the phenotype, or trees from a similar group. Pollen from ripe flowers is thereby collected and then inserted, with a syringe, into a bag covering the ovulate flowers. The parents of the resultant seed are known. If the trees from this union have the characteristics of the parental phenotype, they are considered a possible genotype (distinct species). Further testing through several generations is required to prove this hypothesis. It is a slow process, and no doubt some branching habits will not be attributed directly to known factors of environment or inheritance. What else, then, could be the cause?

That heredity is really unimportant is exemplified by the soybean. One Oriental variety, when grown in light from which the blue-violet end of the spectrum has been eliminated, becomes a twiner. Other closely related plants, like four-o'clocks, treated the same way do not become twiners. Nor do the soybeans twine in ordinary light. This interaction of species or variety and light shows the importance of environmental factors in bringing out hereditary characteristics.

As an afterthought, the ecologist wonders why poison ivy occurs as climbing vine and as stalk plant in the same stand and apparently under nearly identical conditions. Is there a slight variation in the environment, unknown at present, which may account for this, or do certain seeds of *Rhus toxicodendron* carry erect genes, while others have a twining factor?

Radiation Effects

Radiation by subatomic particles has probably from the very time of creation played an important role in the alteration of plants. The dramatic effect of intense gamma (X) radiation on (1) seed viability, or life, (2) growth rates of plants from irradiated seed, and (3) mutations that arise from seed so treated, as well as (4) the effect of the energy of a cobalt 60 source on wood cells in living trees—all seem to attest to this. Genes are thus modified by high-energy subatomic radiation.

Carbon 14, a radioactive isotope, occurs naturally in the carbon dioxide of the air we breathe and of the gas we exhale in respiration. In contrast with that of the laboratory tests, this radiation is dilute and its energy—a beta ray—is weak. Nevertheless, it is hypothesized that over the ages even this relatively inconsequential nuclear energy source could result in the formation of mutations, as well as in the elimination of species or varieties (as we know them in an artificial classification system).

The Creator of the universe turned loose this radiation for a purpose. He also turned man loose to learn that purpose. The botanical ecologist is very curious to know what effect it has had, and continues to have, on the occurrence and frequency of plants and types of plants in the community. This is another significant problem whose solution we are awaiting, if not with bated breath, at least with animated expectation.

Polyploidy (Multiple Chromosomes)

Some trees in the forest, especially the cone-bearing trees, are diploid (have a double arrangement)—*i.e.*, certain cells resulting from sexual fertilization have twice the number of chromosomes as in normal mature sex cells of either sex. The normal is not always the rule. Slash pines and aspens sometimes have *more* than twice this number. Why this happens is again not known. Characteristics of such trees are sometimes freakish abnormalities in growth and form, such as stunting, thick fleshy needles, and unusual foliage color. For slash pine, the frequency of polyploidy, as determined in nursery beds where 1,000,000 seedlings per acre are grown, is 0.0002 percent. The affected stock has depressed root and shoot growth; pollen grains are abortive, leaving seeds empty; and survival chances are poor. Polyploidy can be induced by physicochemical means. This knowledge may be helpful in deciphering the mechanism of this aberrant induction in nature. But much more needs to be known.

Carbohydrate Production

The greatest unknown for the botanist is how to make carbohydrate synthetically when given the ingredients used by any green plant for the purpose. Chlorophyll can be prepared in the laboratory. Air gases can be mixed in any proportion, and the energy of light as the catalyst (accelerator) can be provided. Yet carbohydrate just doesn't come out. If the secret unfolded, man could probably feed the world—using a factory the size of a common school building.

To conquer the obstacle, an attack from all sides is required. Any conclusions about the production of carbohydrate are sought; even information on the influence which natural production of the compounds may have on the frequency and abundance of individual plants in a community is sought.

Many carbohydrates and metabolic products—sugars, starch, color pigments, leather-treating tannins, gums, mucilages, and pectin (the gelling property in fruit)—can be isolated in the laboratory. Some can be reconstructed in the laboratory. Still even the origin of some, like the pentose sugars, is unknown. Are they synthesized directly in photosynthesis (a light process), or are they formed from other sugars? It must be mentioned that enzymes are important in carbohydrate production. Their lack in the onion is probably the reason why this member of the lily family does not form starch.

Carbohydrate production and transformation are attributed in some way to the effects of (1) temperature, (2) water, (3) hydrogen ion—an electrified particle—(4) light, (5) nutrition, and (6) oxygen. Thus, (1) winter temperatures convert starch to sugar in plant cells, making certain twigs in winter and cold-stored potatoes sweeter); (2) high water content in leaves gives a stiff starchiness; (3) hydrogen ion concentration in some way controls enzyme reaction; (4) autumnal red—anthocyanin—is produced only in leaves directly exposed to the light; (5) low soil nitrogen encourages anthocyanin—red—pigmentation, and low soil potash discourages chlorophyll production to expose red pigmentation prematurely; and (6) oxygen, as a component of carbohydrate molecules, must, of course, be present in excess. Other factors controlling these reactions are hypothesized (theorized about), and there are many hypotheses (theories) yet to come.

One ecological consideration: Carbon dioxide in the atmosphere is important for photosynthesis (the forming of chemical compounds through light), especially in the forest where the concentration of the gas is variable. It is present in low concentrations in the atmosphere but is required in large amounts for photosynthesis. The air contains about 0.03 percent of carbon dioxide. Rain and fog may increase this concentration appreciably, especially in swamps where organic matter is rapidly being decomposed. The small amount of carbon dioxide in the air is believed to limit photosynthesis. Scotch pine needles, according to a Swedish forester, produce three times the normal photosynthate when carbon dioxide is ten times its normal 0.03 percent content. This should, it seems, result in improved growth of vegetation. Experiments in greenhouses with above-normal carbon dioxide concentrations resulted in greater growth of several herbaceous plants (soft plants, without woody tissue). Books are available on this intriguing subject, with each worker making a contribution, but none as yet able to make food in a "foliage factory."

Lost Pines

A stand of loblolly pines, covering several hundred acres, occurs well beyond the otherwise natural range of the species in Texas. Some believe that this island stand of trees in the dry central Texas hills is a remnant of a finger extending southwestward from the moist mixed pine-hardwood zone of eastern Texas. If this is so, the evidence is not too clear.

Annual rainfall decreases about one inch with each twenty-five miles' distance to the west from the fifty-inch zone of the forested east. Rainfall averages only thirty inches per annum in the Lost Pines. Foresters have long tried to establish conifers in the wastelands in between, but without success. Why then should this strain, although only of slightly poorer form, thrive there? Is it an inherited characteristic which provides drought resistance? Has some natural agent through the ages isolated drought-resistant strains as the climate changed from a mesic (median, or middle) to a xeric (dry) type?

The probability is being studied that drought resistance is the inherited factor to which survival of the species in the granite hills can be ascribed. Tests are under way throughout the *normal natural* range of loblolly pine to determine if survival and early growth are significantly better in droughty summers, which so frequently follow planting. (Only trouble is that so far the summer rains, after the winter planting, have been abundant in all trials.)

The reader will agree that in the realm of plant ecology much is yet to be accomplished before "the dim unknown" becomes less dim or the known opens to the brightness of the morning. But in science, too, "there is nothing covered, that shall not be revealed; and hid, that shall not be known." (Matt. 10:26, AV)

But at God's own time. He is the Supreme Director of nature and the million and one details of nature.

Let scientists bravely exert themselves. They may continue to make great advances, to the Creator's glory and for the widespread benefit of humanity. They may also acquire a deeper and more humbling sense of the Creator's wisdom, of which all human scientific wisdom is but a feeble, blurred, and highly unsteady reflection.

MYSTERIES OF PLANT LIFE—
THE ULTIMATE CAUSE

BY WILLIAM H. VANDEN BORN

PLANT SCIENTIST

CROP ECOLOGIST

Dr. Vanden Born was originally a Canadian immigrant from the Netherlands. He is a product of the fine Christian school system in the Netherlands, and after crossing the Atlantic he entered the University of Alberta, Edmonton, Canada. He graduated with a B.Sc. and an M.Sc. and some years later obtained his Ph.D. degree from the University of Toronto. His native land is known for its intensive scientific agriculture and general thoroughness, and Dr. Vanden Born seems to have absorbed these qualities and applied them to his work, both during his formative academic years and in his teaching capacity. For several years he has been a professor in the Department of Plant Science at the University of Alberta, devoting himself especially to weed science and crop ecology.

THE central aim of scientific activity is to disclose or to elucidate the law structure of God-created reality. In plant ecology we focus our scientific attention on one particular aspect of the whole of reality—namely, on plants and their environmental relationships and responses.

The word "ecology" is related to the more familiar word "economy" and is based, at least in part, on the Greek word *oikos.* Hence, it has reference to the house or household. It has to do with environment and the factors which make up the environment. Plants are "environed" by climate, lakes, rivers, mountains, deserts—and competitors. Plants, much like human beings, respond to changes in the conditions under which they grow, changes in their environment. But they do so in a way vastly different from that of men. The latter, through a variety of technological developments, are able to compensate for deficiencies in their environmental conditions. They are able to modify their environment, as when they build a house, light a fire, or turn on an air conditioner. Plants cannot do any such things. They must get along as well as they can without such artificial protective or modifying devices.

Plants, however, are frequently able to adjust to or to overcome unfavorable conditions or periods of unfavorable conditions remarkably well by means of particular features or structures that they possess. When discussing such features or structures, we must be careful not to become involved in teleological statements about them, such as "a tree sheds its leaves in the fall to avoid having them frozen," or "bean plants push their roots down to get life-giving water and send their stems up for sunlight." Such statements tend to attribute to plants properties of intelligence and purposeful direction which they, of course, do not possess. There is indeed a purpose connected with such development, but it is not a conscious direction-giving purpose within individual plants or their organs.

In our scientific enterprise we observe certain phenomena in nature, in this instance particularly in plants, and by a variety of approaches we try to find exactly how these phenomena are brought about and how they are influenced by different factors. We attempt to explain the phenomena in terms of biophysical and biochemical reactions or laws, and we try to relate these to what is known about the law structure governing plant life. We know that all reality possesses a God-given creational order and that God from day to day upholds reality in accordance with this order. This knowledge gives us confidence in the reliability of the results of our scientific investigation, our attempt to find out something about this creational order, or order of Divinely instituted laws. In many instances this attempt has been relatively successful. In other instances the explanation of the phenomena observed still seems very faraway. I shall describe some of these instances in this chapter.

It is not always possible to define exactly the reason why a certain problem defies scientific explanation. Sometimes such reasons can be pinpointed rather easily, as when attempts are made to explain certain functional aspects of plants or plant organs. To ascribe purpose to specific plant organs or processes is beyond scientific analysis. For example, seed dormancy is said to have survival value, meaning that it enables the plant species involved to survive a period of unfavorable growing conditions. Such a statement describes the situation but is not in any sense a scientific explanation. When purpose and meaning are considered, scientific explanation terminates abruptly. Purpose and meaning are not subject to analysis by scientific experimentation. Rather, they are the subject of religiously directed philosophical consideration.

An important limiting factor in arriving at a satisfactory explanation of biological observations is the fact that we are dealing with living material and that in our experimental techniques this material often has to be killed. Life in plant cells and tissues is intimately dependent on structure and organization. More often than not it is impossible to get at the details of this organization without actually destroying the organization. Improvements in experimental technique will undoubtedly remove at least part of this limitation, but it is not likely to be done away with entirely.

What, then, are some of these unsolved and perhaps, for the present, unsolvable problems?

Life cycles of plants have no real beginning or end, but in terms of the growth cycle during a particular season the seed is an appropriate place to begin our considerations. Previously I referred to the problem of seed dormancy. Seeds are said to be dormant when under conditions normally favorable to germination they fail to germinate. This characteristic of dormancy is peculiar to seeds of a variety of plant species. It is particularly evident in seeds soon after they have been formed. Dormancy in seeds has what is called survival value because seeds formed in plants in late summer, if dormant, will not germinate until at least the following growing season and often not until even more time has elapsed. If germination should occur as soon as the seeds fall to the ground, the resulting seedlings would be killed by frost in temperate zones with a marked winter season. In other climatic zones such seedlings might be killed by drought, if a dry period followed the normal growing season.

Under natural conditions dormant seeds in most instances gradually lose their dormancy. In some seeds, for example, dormancy is caused by the inability of water to penetrate the seed coat. As the seeds lie in the soil, in time the seed coat begins to break down and becomes permeable to water. Water is essential for seed germination. In other seeds a chemical substance which inhibits germination and growth may be present in the seed coat. As such seeds lie in or on the soil, the inhibitor is gradually leached out of the seed coat or is broken down by chemical reactions. Sooner or later there comes a time when the inhibitor is no longer present in a high enough concentration to stop seed germination, and growth can proceed.

In a number of plant species we happen to know the causal factors in this seed dormancy. There are many species, however, whose seeds exhibit what is called physiological dormancy. This means little more than that we don't really know what brings about the dormancy or the loss of it, although we know a great deal about how to influence it. We know of several means by which the period of dormancy can be shortened. We can do so, for example, by exposing the seeds to a low temperature, just above freezing, for a period of time or by treating them with an appropriate chemical substance, such as gibberellin. But we don't know just what these treatments do to the seed and how they help overcome dormancy. Nor do we know how the dormancy of such seeds is overcome under natural conditions. A variety of things have been measured in seeds during the time in which the "depth" of dormancy is gradually decreasing, but in no cases have these observed changes formed a meaningful pattern which could be related to known physiological or biochemical processes. The mystery persists.

Most plants, but not all, begin their life history as a small seedling from a germinating seed. As soon as the seedling begins to grow into a plant, the various factors that make up the environment of the plant begin to play their roles, and it is in some of these individual factors that further mysterious problems present themselves.

One of the factors that have puzzled research workers for many years is the resistance of plants to high or low temperatures. Generally, plants grow well only within a limited range of temperatures. When they are exposed to temperatures that are well below or well above this biological range, the plants usually do not survive. Some plants, however, have peculiar properties, in the sense that they are able to tolerate either extremely high or extremely low temperatures without suffering severe injury. Differences in behavior of plant species are particularly noticeable in the case of resistance to frost—that is, to temperatures below the freezing point of water.

Most plants in an unhardened condition are not able to survive a prolonged period of frost. Water in the plant tissues produces ice crystals, which seriously disrupt cell organization, tend to dehydrate the living matter of the cells, and result in the death of cells and tissues. Ironically, death or severe injury usually does not occur immediately after freezing but only after the tissues have begun to thaw out again. As long as the tissue remains frozen, the cells and the tissue structure remain virtually intact.

Numerous experiments have been made in an attempt to determine what changes occur in plant cells or in plant organs during the period of hardening (plant tissue acquiring firmness or rigidity). Many changes have been observed, in both physical and chemical organization of the tissue, but no satisfactory pattern of changes that account for all the mutations observed has yet been established. Some plants, at least during certain stages of development, are able to acquire a high degree of frost resistance during a period of hardening. Other plants may never become hardy, no matter how long the hardening period lasts. As in the case of seed dormancy referred to previously, we know a great deal about the various factors that influence the hardening process and frost resistance, and in some plant species we are able to manipulate these almost at will; but we are still in the dark about the exact mechanisms which account for these properties.

At the other end of the scale is resistance to extremely *high* temperatures. When plant cells and tissues are exposed to temperatures well above the normal range, they usually die or suffer severe injury. In most instances such death or injury has been attributed to denaturation (loss of some original properties) and coagulation (clotting) of the essential proteins in the cells. Peculiarly enough, however, there are some plants that are extremely resistant to high temperatures, while other plants are badly injured even by moderately high temperatures. As with frost resistance, here also we know a good deal about various factors that may influence the degree of heat resistance in different species, but we know very little about the exact mechanism that gives a plant the property of resistance to high temperatures other than an apparently safe supposition that there is a difference in the properties of the cellular proteins of these plants. But this is really nothing more than a conjecture and provides no real explanation.

An example of the ability to adjust to unfavorable environmental conditions is the ability of some plants to regulate the amount of water used by them in accordance with the available supply. This adjustment is made mainly by controlling the amount of water they lose to the atmosphere. Some plants reduce their water loss by having their leaves roll up, thus reducing the surface area exposed to the atmosphere; in others the stomata, the openings through which water vapor is lost, may remain closed; and still others may actually shed a number of their leaves under conditions of water stress. Plants are known to exhibit this type of behavior, but when it comes to an explanation of these adjustments, we are still very far from knowing exactly what reactions in the plant bring about their occurrence. The condition of water stress must produce within the plant some type of reaction which, in turn, brings about the observed response. Perhaps we should call it a chain of reactions, triggered by the initial stimulus of water stress. When the water supply once again becomes adequate, the reverse reaction takes place. Plants begin to grow again, buds develop into new leaves, flowers and fruits are produced, and another cycle of growth can be completed. Much information, by the way, is available about the length of time different plants can endure water stress before reaching a point of no return.

The types of behavior under water stress that I have described are actually the results of mechanisms by which the plant escapes internal drought. Most plant species cannot long survive even partial dehydration of their tissues. There are marked differences, however, in the actual degree of dehydration that different plants can tolerate without suffering permanent injury. Why should this be the case if plant cells have, in general at least, the same kind of components? Various theories, attempting an answer to this question, have come and gone, but as yet no entirely satisfactory explanation is available. Differences in degree of drought resistance may be referred to the category of differences in protoplasmic structure (inner cell structure), but this can hardly be called an explanation. Our unsolved problems are multiplying!

Not only are plants able to withstand drought with varying degrees of success, but they also have substantially different abilities to extract water from the soil. These differences in efficiency of water uptake are in many instances a direct result of the extent of development of the root system of the plant. Even with the same total length of root system, however, the roots of one plant may be able to reduce the water content of the soil to a much lower level than those of another plant.

The extent of root development in dry soil is a problem that has stirred up a good deal of interest among scientists. It has frequently been observed that when plants grow in soil that is relatively dry, the root system will continue to develop until the tips of the roots reach a layer of soil that contains an adequate amount of water. If such a moist layer happens to be close to the plant, the root system may not develop very extensively at all. If, on the other hand, the moist layer is some distance away from the plant or, rather, from the surface of the soil, the roots may have to grow through dry soil for a considerable distance before they reach the moist layer. The extent of such growth is, of course, limited by the availability of moisture close to the base of the plant. A light rain, for example, would reach only the surface layers of the soil. Root development may also be checked by other resources, such as reserve food material that the plant has available. Much of these root growth phenomena is truly enigmatic. It represents not one but several problems.

In temperate regions there is usually a distinct seasonal difference in plant life. One season may be very suitable for plant growth and development, while another season may be entirely unsuitable. The question that has puzzled plant ecologists and physiologists for many centuries is: How do plants prepare for such periods of unfavorable conditions?

Much experimental work has been done to find a satisfactory answer to this question. At present we know a good deal about the various factors that may influence such preparation processes. But we still know next to nothing about the actual mechanisms involved. We know how different conditions may affect the rate of preparation for an unfavorable period, but beyond that we know precious little. During such a season of unfavorable conditions plants are said to be dormant—that is, they continue to live, but they do not actively produce new growth. As a result of experimental work in recent years, many plants which normally have an annual dormant period can be induced to grow more or less continuously under certain conditions. Also, in almost all plants that periodically become dormant a state of dormancy can be induced even in the season during which there is normally active growth. This can be done by changing the external conditions. Factors such as temperature, photoperiod (light period), quality of light, temperature during the light and dark periods, nutritive conditions, and water supply are among those which greatly influence growth activity. The combined effect of these factors determines the growth response of the plants.

In general, scientists have made great progress in the study of plant life. Along with other natural sciences the science of plant ecology has learned a very great deal about God's wonderworld in the past few decades. But the thing that has stopped us too often and still stops us again and again is the inner mechanisms of plant life that I have referred to repeatedly in this writing. We still face problems, intricate and unsolved problems—and many of them—in this advanced age.

Yet in closing, let me say that I believe there are no problems that can be tagged as permanently and forever unsolvable. Our scientific investigations should continue, in an authentic way, and should be aimed at discovering the law structure of reality that exists because of God's creational order. All things are subject to the law of the Creator, and for this reason both the interrelatedness of all things and our ability to obtain scientific knowledge are guaranteed. Within the framework of that creational order all scientific

103]

problems are *potentially* solvable, and the chief limitation is the present inability of scientists to apprehend, by instrument and experiment, all the many and various details of the law structure. We shall never fully know all of God's natural laws in the present scheme of things. Man, in his present estate, is imperfect. His imperfections constitute the ultimate cause of his deficient knowledge in natural science, including the science of plant ecology.

Even so, God has graciously given man both ability and opportunity to investigate His creation and to carry on research unceasingly for His greater glory and man's benefit. He has given us the responsibility to press on in the search for knowledge, also in the rich and wide realm of plants.

For that we are grateful. And as we proceed, humbly but zealously, we pray for His indispensable guidance and blessing.

CELLS, THE AMAZING ABODE
OF LIFE

BY GEORGE F. HOWE

CYTOLOGIST

Dr. Howe is a Christian scholar of great capability. The science of biology is in his blood, and cytology, or cell science, especially has the love of his heart. He was graduated with high honors and a B.Sc. from Wheaton College, Illinois, and thereafter went to Ohio State University, where he was a Charles F. Kettering Fellow and was graduated with both M.Sc. and Ph.D. degrees. His specialty at Ohio State was photosynthesis in the leaves of higher plants. For several years he has been a professor of biology at Westmount College, in California, and is now the chairman in that school of the Division of Natural Science. He is a member of the Ohio Academy of Science, the American Society of Plant Physiologists, and several other high-grade scientific organizations.

BIOLOGIC study during the past century and a half has driven men repeatedly to the conclusion that life ultimately resides in miniature parcels, known as cells. After the development of the microscope man's eye focused on the form and composition of the cellular threads in the living fabric, only to find them housing an astonishing array of interdependent equipment. Especially three men—Henri Dutrochet, French army surgeon; Matthias Schleiden, German lawyer-botanist; and Theodor Schwann, German physiologist—foresaw the cell as the vital unit. Their simple nineteenth-century dictum "Life is cellular" has led to cell science, or cytology—an important branch of twentieth-century biology.

It is now understood that any large living structure, such as a tree leaf or a human brain, is built of minute cellular bricks. Each animated brick exposes a detailed architecture of its own. Every answer yielded by diligent cytological research opens newer and more baffling questions. The biblical writer anticipated this great, incalculable intricacy of God's craftsmanship when he wrote, "Then I beheld all the work of God, that a man cannot find out the work that is done under the sun: because though a man labor to seek it out, yet he shall not find it. . . ." (Eccles. 8:17, AV)

General Cell Structure

Before posing cytological questions, let us look at cell structure in general. Most cells consist of several overall regions. The outer portion of the cell substance is what we call a cytoplasmic membrane, which has the mysterious capacity of allowing certain chemical substances free passage, while maintaining a virtual closed-door policy to other materials. In addition to this filmy covering, some cells have an exterior cell wall composed of cellulose fibers and other constituents.

Covered by the cytoplasmic membrane and continuous with it is the jellylike cytoplasm itself. Far from being an unstructured matrix, cytoplasm manifests internal order and numerous particulate bodies. The gummy cytoplasm is transversed by a finely structured interweaving network of membranes, known as the endoplasmic reticulum. On the interlacing sheets of the reticulum are hung myriads of beadlike ribosomes. Possibly ribosomes act as the sites of synthesis (combination) of complex cellular protein molecules. Shaped like miniature potatoes, rods, or spheres, other particles, called mitochondria, contain the chemical accessories (enzymes) involved in the burning of fuel and the liberation of packaged cellular energy. Plant cell cytoplasm sometimes has green bodies (frequently disk-shaped), which hold crystalline systems of chlorophyll molecules (green coloring matter of plants). Such chloroplast bodies convert light energy into the packaged chemical energy of glucose sugar.

Some cells maintain one or more internal watery regions encased by other membranes. The solution in these vacuoles (cavities) contains many salts, sugars, and acids. Vacuoles in plants play a role in the uptake of water by osmosis (absorption through partly permeable membranes). They may also serve as storage sites for cell products and waste materials. Some vacuoles in certain microorganisms undergo frequent pulsations, thereby excreting or pumping wastes and excess water from the cells.

Engulfed by the cytoplasm is an object, shaped like a slightly flattened sphere, known as the cell nucleus. A covering, called the nuclear membrane or envelope, seems to have direct contact and continuity with the endoplasmic reticulum mentioned previously in connection with the cytoplasm. The nuclear envelope houses several finger-shaped chromosomes that carry the reproductive code of life and the chemical information essential to protein manufacture in ribosomes. (The number of chromosomes present varies from species to species.) If the cytoplasm and its particles may be likened to a cellular factory, then the nucleus appears to serve as a biological board of directors.

The Wonders of Cell Structure

We now consider some of the problems that face a cytologist. We might expect that of all the parts surveyed, the cellulose cell wall would be the least likely to present a serious challenge to a biologist's understanding. Yet this prosaic coating manifests a puzzle still unsolved by the keenest minds. Although apparently rigid, the wall expands as a young plant

107]

cell grows. A child's leather shoe that would wonderfully spread, repair itself, and maintain its thickness as the foot enlarged would be something like a cell wall. Does the wall grow by insertion of new fibers into the old wall at seams or patches here and there that supposedly loosen up? Or does the old cellulose remain intact and become uniformly stretched as new layers are applied on the surface during cell expansion?

Some workers have demonstrated a tie between plant growth hormone (indole-3-acetic acid) and cell wall expansion, but no one knows how the hormone works. Does the wall actively grow in response to the hormone (thus itself leading the process), or does it simply enlarge passively when the growing cell exerts a pressure from within? The "how" of cell wall growth still remains unknown.

Intricate questions such as these posed by a cell wall testify to the Divine Inventor's creative genius in originating and maintaining such processes. The Apostle Paul deals with this very matter in his Epistle to the Colossians when he presents Christ as the key to the sustenance of the universe and its life processes. He says, speaking of Christ, "and he is before all things, and *in* him all things consist." (Ch. 1:17, ASV) Commenting on these words, the great New Testament scholar J. B. Lightfoot has said, "He (Christ) is the principle of cohesion in the universe. He impresses upon creation that unity and solidarity which makes it a cosmos instead of a chaos. Thus (to take one instance) the action of gravitation, which keeps in their places things fixed and regulates the motions of things moving, is an expression of *His* mind."

Cytology has generated some heated debates. One controversy arose concerning certain cytoplasmic areas that darken in the presence of silver or osmium ions (osmium is a hard metallic element of the platinum group, and an ion is an electrified particle). These cell areas were clearly described in 1898 by the Italian scientist Camillo Golgi, while he was working with brain cells of the barn owl. Later some other workers firmly maintained that Golgi bodies did not really exist in living cells but originated as artifacts (artificial bodies), formed when fat globules combined with silver ions. Although some questions about their nature still exist, they have now become clearly visible under the electron microscope. There is also evidence that these puzzling structures can be separated from other cell particles by centrifugation —a scientific procedure not unlike the separation of butterfat from milk by a whirling cream centrifuge. Identified in various plant and animal cells, Golgi bodies are usually seen as a stack of flattened parallel sacs associated with swollen vacuoles (cavities) of various sizes.

Golgi bodies demonstrate no unique biochemical syntheses (combinations). Upon discovering Golgi bodies in cottonseed embryo sacs, one worker suggested that they may help nourish the egg cell. Because the Golgi bodies are well developed in cells that actively secrete (for example, pancreas cells that manufacture insulin), some workers theorize that they act somehow as areas of collection and packaging for cellular secretions. But they are still a problem. The exact roles and ultimate structure of the Golgi bodies are still in doubt. An exhaustive catalogue of all Golgi functions in various cell types has not been written, nor has the origin of the Golgi body been adequately traced.

Then there are the lysosomes. If Golgi bodies are like cellular produce-packaging plants (maybe), then lysosomes may serve as cytoplasmic policemen or miniature scavengers. Christian de Duve and others have recorded lysosomes of various shapes in cells of the kidney, spleen, thyroid, plant meristem (embryonic tissue), and certain protozoa (minute single-cell animals). Lysosomes apparently consist of a single outer membrane housing a potent fluid that is known to be rich in destructive hydrolase and acid phosphatase enzymes (chemical ferment). Such chemical enzyme molecules are capable of hastening the breakdown of proteins, carbohydrates, nucleic acids, and organic compounds of sulfur and phosphorus. Dr. de Duve has described lysosomes as "tiny bags filled with a droplet of powerful digestive juice capable of breaking down most of the constituents of living matter." (*Scientific American*, Vol. 208, No. 5, p. 64)

What part could such deadly vesicles (tiny bladders) ever play in a living system? Probable lysosome functions include: (1) the self-digestion of dead or exhausted cells, (2) the destruction of invading bacteria, (3) the liberation of food within a cell itself by controlled digestion during starvation, and (4) the destruction of dangerous foreign proteins that may enter the body.

Attending the few facts that are partially understood about lysosomes are numerous unsolved problems. A few of these include such conundrums as: (1) What is the origin of the lysosome membrane—or the lysosome itself, for that matter? (2) What governs controlled lysosome activity during starvation and the rupture of membranes at cell death? (3) What undetermined properties of the lysosome membrane make it impervious to its own vitriolic contents?

Certain cells have one filamentous flagellum or many fingerlike cilia that extend from within the cell through the exterior medium like tiny whips. A typical cilium (hairlike growth) or flagellum (whiplike growth) sliced in cross section and studied with an electron microscope reveals eleven internal cables. Nine of the cables are symmetrically spaced in a peripheral ring, and two extra cables are located in the center. (Some cilia lack the pair of central strands.) Cilium design resembles the complicated substructure of a telephone cable, in which many smaller parallel fibers make up one larger strand. No one understands the full significance of the eleven inner filaments, although it is believed that they play some role in the movement of cilia. The amazing cellular appendages keep bending from base to tip and back again.

In a multicellular animal, cilia are present only on certain cells within the body. Keeping this in mind, we may note that ciliated cells are widely distributed, being present somewhere in the bodies of organisms representing most groups of the animal kingdom. Certain plant types also have cilia.

The numerous cilia that cover a one-celled paramecium (minute water animal) beat in coordination, enabling this microorganism to dart spirally forward and backward in response to such factors as heat, light, and food. Cilia covering surface cells in the human windpipe flex in rhythmic waves forcing dust or bacteria out of the respiratory tract. Cilia on fish gills act as miniature water pumps. What directs the cilia on various cells to fill these and other roles? What unknown system coordinates the intricate movements of cilia? What are the origin and ultimate meaning of the consistent nine-two order of the internal strands? These and other problems await the scientists who are patient enough to work with motile hairs so small that several hundred may cover the surface of a single cell!

But the believers in biblical theism are not really surprised at such carefully and marvelously detailed architecture in the world of living cells. This intricate pattern of design points clearly to their incomparable Designer. The Bible expresses it in this manner: ". . . every house is builded by some man; but he that built all things is God." (Heb. 3:4, AV)

Problems in Cell Reproduction

Additional problems are encountered in the matter of cell reproduction. Such reproduction usually occurs by a simple division of one cell into two daughter cells. Preexisting cytoplasm going to each daughter cell carries with it many substances—ribosomes, mitochondria, and chloroplasts. By mechanisms not clearly comprehended, it is theorized that old mitochondria and chloroplasts reproduce by yielding identical new particles. Perhaps old particles contain coded receipts for self-reproduction.

Cell separation follows one of two characteristic patterns.

Between two newly formed animal cells a cleavage furrow deepens from the outside, eventually pinching the old cell into two individual units, much as one could divide a lump of soft dough by squeezing inward with the fingers. Plant cells, on the other hand, generally divide from the inside out by a division plate that separates the old cell into two distinct halves, just as one might partition a large room by erecting a new center wall. What triggers and governs the division plate formation in plants? Certain parts of the cell are believed to be involved somehow, but no final answer has been found. Why do plant cells divide one way characteristically and animal cells another? Again we are minus an answer.

Clearly seen in the cells of animals and certain plants is a mysterious object shaped like a tiny barrel—the centriole. Centrioles, which have a typical nine-two internal fiber arrangement, are thought to generate cell cilia by some unknown sequence. Just before a cell nucleus divides, the centriole lying outside the nucleus mysteriously reproduces, and daughter centrioles then take positions at opposite sides, or poles, of the nucleus.

By a sequence not yet discovered, each centriole yields a cone of many attaching spindle fibers, and each fiber extends to the equator of the cell. The nuclear membrane concurrently disappears, and the chromosomes, which hitherto had only a vague outline, take on the definite appearance of discrete elongated bodies. Moving under the influence of some inexplicable force, chromosomes migrate to the central ring formed by the juncture of opposite spindle cones.

Very little is known about the physical structure or chemical nature of spindle fibers. Their form and behavior may have something to do with organic sulfur compounds discovered in the fibers. How does an entire spindle apparatus appear when needed during division and later apparently vanish? How can spindle fibers form within some plant cells in which no centrioles can be seen?

Having moved to a central position, chromosomes hover in a ring at the equator, or central region, of the cell. Each chromosome has been seen to be actually not one but two duplicate daughter chromosomes held together. Presently, as if responding to some inaudible signal and drawn by some unseen magnets, the connected daughter chromosomes separate and migrate. From a side view chromosomes traveling to opposite cell poles look somewhat like football players returning from the line of scrimmage to form a backfield huddle as a sudden time-out whistle blows. How do chromosomes move? Are they pulled apart by attaching spindle fibers serving as miniature muscles or rubber bands? Is the motivating force mechanical, chemical, or electrical? Does the dotlike centromere found on each daughter chromosome somehow serve as a small organ of motility, pulling the chromosome through the cell?

Duplicate daughter chromosome sets clustered at opposite ends of the cell are finally covered by new membranes and eventually become individual nuclei in the two new and separate cells. How is the complex division of the nucleus geared to the simultaneous cleavage of the cytoplasm so that in most organisms each daughter cell receives a duplicated nucleus?

From start to finish the division of a cell is a wondrous event. It is by repetition of this phenomenon that a single fertilized egg cell produces the astronomical spectrum of cells composing a human body. A twentieth-century knowledge of cell division would only have added to the psalmist's awe as he contemplated God's role in governing the formation of an embryo: ". . . thou hast covered me in my mother's womb. . . . My substance was not hid from thee, when I was made in secret, and curiously wrought in the lowest parts of the earth. Thine eyes did see my substance, yet being unperfect; and in thy book all my members were written, which in continuance were fashioned, when as yet there was none of them." (Ps. 139:13, 15, 16, AV)

At this point we might mention that the mysteries surrounding cancer are somehow linked to cell reproduction. The frequency of division usually decreases in cells of adults.

The ability of cells in adult organisms to divide is not totally lost, however, but seems to be checked by some unidentified controlling system. As A. B. Pardee says in a National Cancer Institute monograph, "Perhaps the most fundamental characteristic of cancer is that the cells fail to stop dividing, while the normal cell's growth is limited." (*N.C.I. Monograph 14*, p. 8)

What causes certain cells to proliferate to the detriment of the entire organism? Does cancer result from a disorganized pattern of fuel consumption in the mitochondria, as one group of workers believed? Does cancer develop from any derangement in a theoretical check-and-balance system that body cells may exert on one another? Is there any consistent link between viruses and cancer? Are chromosome changes somehow involved in producing the disease? These perplexing puzzles, related to cell division, await future solution.

The study of cancer itself and the nature of all disease bring us inevitably face to face with the philosophical question of biologic evil. Why are suffering, disease, decay, and death present in a system that is otherwise harmonious? Although a detailed analysis is beyond the scope of this chapter, the writer is firmly convinced that the Word of God lays down specific guidelines for building coherent answers to the question of biologic evil. (See Gen. 3; Rom. 5:12-21; and I Cor. 15:21,22.)

The Enigma of Cell Change

Individual cells in a typical growing zone, such as an onion stem tip, are originally nearly all alike in size, shape, and structure. As the organ enlarges, diverse patterns of growth lead cells to change or differentiate one from another. Stem surface cells devoid of chloroplasts differentiate, forming a flat, living skin—the epidermis. Some cells underneath produce numerous chloroplasts and finally enlarge into robust sugar factories—chlorenchyma. Certain other cell groups within the stem unite yielding a complex cable or vascular bundle. Within the bundle some cells elongate, thicken their walls, and become spindle-shaped supporting fibers. Others arranged in vertical columns elongate, lose their end walls, and die, forming xylem or water vessels. Other columns of cells produce vertical phloem or food-carrying elements. Differentiation in animal embryos likewise manifests changes whereby neighboring cells specialize.

The question naturally is, What governs the diversification of seemingly similar cells? No doubt hormones and cell position are somehow involved. But the details of differentiation elude man's grasp. This, too, is still an unsolved problem.

A cell once specialized may again generalize and reproduce, thus showing that cells are essentially totipotent (having general capability). F. C. Steward has shown that individual cells from root bundles in a carrot plant divide when freed from their neighbors and cultured in a coconut milk medium. One cell yields a cluster that finally develops into an organized carrot plant! Dr. Steward describes the new plant as "in all respects a normal carrot plant which will mature and produce a storage organ, flowers, and seeds." (*Science magazine,* Vol. 143, No. 3601 pp. 20-26)

Totipotency is also noted in sphagnum mosses, in which one cell separated from a "leaf" will regenerate an entire moss plant. Somehow the blueprint for a complete adult is confined in one lone cell!

What is it about coconut milk that liberates the hidden potentials of cells? If each cell is indeed totipotent, how are cells in a developing organism guided and kept as specialized subsidiary units of various tissues? How can something as small as a cell with its chromosomes carry all the plans for building a body? Unanswerable questions, all, at least in this present "advanced" modern age.

In this brief chapter we have reviewed only a few of the great unknowns facing cytologists. Man has not penetrated and comprehended the origin, operation, and ultimate organization of such cellular portions as cell walls, Golgi bodies, lysosomes, cilia, and flagella. Whole clusters of problems still remain unsolved in the areas of cell reproduction, cancer, differentiation, and totipotency. But such architectural innovation, diversity, and microengineering as *can* be seen and understood about living cells should cause us to join the psalmist in exclaiming: "I will praise thee; for I am fearfully and wonderfully made: marvelous are thy works; and that my soul knoweth right well. . . . How precious also are thy thoughts unto me, O God! How great is the sum of them! If I should count them, they are more in number than the sand: when I awake, I am still with thee." (Ps. 139: 14, 17, 18, AV)

It is important to realize that the Eternal Craftsman has a continuing interest in His handiwork and a spiritual plan for man, His supreme earthly creation. The Apostle Paul summed it up in his great address to the people of Athens, Greece (Acts 17). He declared God to be the Sovereign Creator of the universe and all it contains, its Divine Sustainer, and the Author and Establisher of natural laws, including the laws of life and growth, and he summoned uninformed, baffled men to turn to Christ, the Truth of God and the Life of God. Although biological life may forever remain a complex cellular riddle, God's provision for man's spiritual, eternal life is clear and wonderfully simple.

THE GREAT HIDDEN WORLD
THAT IS YOU AND I

BY LION F. GARDINER

ZOOLOGIST

CYTOLOGIST

In addition to extensive studies in zoology, this writer has devoted many years to the study of cell biology. With a B.Sc. from Wheaton College and an M.Sc. from the University of Michigan, he has taught at the University of Michigan, at Delta College, in Michigan, and at the University of Rhode Island. As a zoologist and cytologist, his primary interest has been in marine life and environment, and he is still in the thick of this exciting subject. He is a member of the American Association for the Advancement of Science, the American Institute of Biological Sciences, the American Scientific Affiliation, the Ecological Society of America, and the American Society of Limnology and Oceanography, and is a researcher in the ecology of benthonic marine invertebrates.

DR. ABRAHAM KUYPER, a brilliant Dutch scholar, has said, "God is so very great in the very small," and anyone who has studied cell science or has merely dabbled in it and has a spark of faith in him will respond to that with a hearty "How true!" Already the men of ancient Bible times, notably King David in the Book of Psalms, knew the truth of this quotation and wrote about its truth, and all through succeeding ages man's knowledge of God's greatness in the very small things of life increased. But it was not until the advanced development of the microscope that this knowledge of man came to a sudden burst, an expansion that the ancients never dreamed of.

The study of cells practically waited for the invention and development of the microscope. Zacharias Janssen, a Hollander, built the first compound microscopic instrument around the year 1590, and another Hollander, Anton van Leeuwenhoek, about a half century later made the first microscope through which microorganisms could be observed. Since then, further modification and perfection of the light microscope have taken place, and these last 30 years have seen the development of the electron microscope. This instrument has a resolving power (ability to distinguish between two objects) of up to 100 times that of the best light microscopes. Other techniques, such as the use of radioisotope tracers and the separation of cellular constituents by high-speed ultracentrifugation (forces obtained up to several hundred thousand times that of gravity), have been very useful for the cellular biologist in discovering the ultrastructure and functioning of the cell.

To get down to the cell—the cell is the basic structural unit of living organisms. Protozoans, or acellular animals, often have only a single cell. An adult human being, however, has about 100 trillion cells—truly "the great hidden world that is you and I." (A trillion is 1,000,000 times 1,000,000.) Of course, the blue whale, the world's largest animal (100 feet in length), has many more cells.

Biological function ultimately takes place at the cellular level. We eat so that our cells will have the necessary raw materials from which to produce energy and synthesize the chemical compounds needed for growth and repair. The oxygen we breathe is available for use in intracellular chemical reactions, and it is in the cell that metabolic wastes are produced. Cells range in size upward from about 0.004 millimeter, and many types are of this size. Each cell is bounded

[118

by a plasma membrane so thick—or, rather, so thin—that we ordinary mortals have a hard time to comprehend it. For expert mathematicians, the third dimension (thickness) of the usual cell wall is about 0.0000075 millimeter.

The cell's membrane is of great importance because it separates the contents of the cell from its external environment. An internal microenvironment, in which a very large number of chemical reactions take place, is thus formed. The membrane is of particular interest to the biologist, for in addition to giving shape to the cell, it regulates the passage of all materials that enter or leave the cell. This greatly influences the cell's internal functioning.

Cellular membranes are thought to contain a number of proteins and lipids (fatty compounds). When stained and photographed by means of the electron microscope, the membrane appears in cross section as two dark lines separated by a lighter band. Several explanations have been proposed for this structure. The most popular is that the membrane is like a sandwich of two single layers of protein molecules separated by a double layer of lipid (fatty) molecules. Its *exact* structure, however, is not definitely known. We cannot be sure that the present explanation is correct or even that measurements made from photomicrographs (photographs taken by means of a microscope) are absolutely accurate, because the cells may be altered somewhat during processing for photographing, when the tissue is killed, stained, and sliced.

Just as there is doubt about the exact structure of the plasma membrane, so there is doubt about its function. Let's look at an example. As we have seen, all materials entering the cell must pass through the membrane and are thus regulated by it. Water molecules move freely through the membrane in both directions by the process of osmosis (absorption through partly permeable membranes). Net flow is down a concentration gradient from a region of higher concentration of water molecules to a region of lower concentration. This occurs passively—that is, the energy necessary to produce the movement is inherent in the water molecules themselves. Other molecules, such as various alcohols and sugars, pass into the cell with varying ease, their rates of passage depending on their characteristics, such as molecular size, solubility in lipids (remember that lipids are constituents of the plasma membrane), and electric charge density. Here, as in the case of water, the process is passive, no energy input being necessary, and net flow progresses down a concentration gradient.

But many materials do not behave in this manner. They accumulate within the cell regardless of concentration gradient. Additional energy must be used to do this, and the process needed and used is known as active transport. Energy bound in a certain type of molecule (known to biologists as ATP molecules) is released for various sorts of cellular work. In biological terminology, ATP is broken down into ADP and P. Biologists know that ATP energy is used for active transport because if the chemical reactions that produce ATP are poisoned, active transport stops.

Active transport is vitally important for the proper functioning of the cells and thus for the entire organism. It is by means of active transport that sodium ions (electrified particles) are pumped out of nerve cells and potassium ions are allowed to accumulate on the inside of the cellular membrane. The electric potential (voltage) difference built up at the surface of the cell by this mechanism makes possible the initiation and conduct of all nerve impulses. Similar impulses carried by muscle cells provide for their contraction at the proper time. It is by means of active transport that many materials needed by an animal are reabsorbed into its blood after having been removed in its kidneys.

A number of models attempting to explain active transport have been proposed. In a particularly popular one a hypothetical carrier molecule in the plasma membrane picks up a molecule of the substance to be transported at the outer edge of the membrane, carries it through the membrane, and, after releasing it on the inside of the cell, returns to the

[120

outside for another one. The carrier molecule, however, hasn't been definitely isolated, and this explanation is still hypothetical. Even if the carrier hypothesis is correct, other questions remain to be answered. There are still unsolved problems. For instance, what sort of complex is formed by the two molecules? Where is ATP energy being used—in forming the complex, in moving the complex through the membrane, or in dissociating the two molecules at the inner surface of the membrane?

Animals vary tremendously in size, size being dependent on the number of cells of which they are composed. Most animals start life as a single cell—the fertilized egg, or zygote. For growth to occur, then, cells must multiply greatly. In addition, they are constantly dying and being worn away and must be replaced. Multiplication is accomplished by a cell's simply dividing into two equal parts, a process called mitosis. The rate of mitosis varies considerably. Some cells in the brain do not reproduce at all in adults. Other cells multiply at exceptionally high rates (10,000,000 per second for human red blood cells).

Inside the plasma membrane of the cell is a thick fluid mixture of many types of chemical compounds, the cytoplasm. Suspended in the cytoplasm are numerous subcellular organs, or organelles, that are responsible for carrying out the many specialized functions of the cell. One of these organelles, the nucleus, is a large, more or less centrally located body surrounded by a double membrane. The nucleus plays a very significant role in the life of the cell and, ultimately, of the organism. It contains the long dark-stained chromosomes. These structures, composed of protein and a certain acid, known as DNA, are known to contain the paired hereditary determiners, or genes. About 30,000 of these pairs are present in the human cell. All cellular structure is determined by the coded message present in the DNA molecules making up the genes. The characteristics of the offspring of organisms depend on the kinds of genes passed on to them in the sperm and egg cells of their parents.

During mitosis (cell division and multiplication) marked changes can be observed in the structure of a cell viewed through a microscope. Among other things, the chromosomes double in number and line up across the center of the cell. Then they divide into two identical groups, and these groups move toward opposite sides of the cell. This having been accomplished, the cytoplasm divides from the circumference of the cell inward and is separated into two parts, and thus two identical daughter cells are formed. Each of these has the same amount of DNA as the original cell, as well as the same number and types of genes.

Mitosis is indeed a remarkable operation, not only for increasing the number of cells, but also for ensuring *exact* reproduction of the hereditary material (DNA). A special modification of mitosis, named meiosis, which occurs only in the reproductive organs, produces the sex cells and ensures that only *one-half* of the parental DNA goes to each cell. Thus, when fertilization takes place, the offspring have the *same* number of genes as their parents, rather than twice as many. That Divine genius is back of all these intricacies should be perfectly evident to every unprejudiced mind.

The obvious question now is, What causes cells to divide? In tissue cultures (cells growing in nutrient media *outside* the organism) freely dividing cells are thought to be regulated by surface area-volume relationships or perhaps the nuclear-cytoplasmic volume ratio. The cell divides when it reaches a critical size. Perhaps a similar mechanism operates in living animals. In growing embryos, however, certain tissues and organs develop more rapidly than others. What causes the differences in mitotic (division and multiplication) rates? Several hypotheses have been suggested, but ultimately we do not know the mechanism of regulation or, in fact, exactly why cells divide at all. These are unsolved problems. Other questions are: What causes DNA to replicate (duplicate repeatedly)? How are DNA molecules arranged in a chromosome? How do the chromosomes move toward the sides of the dividing cell? What causes meiosis in the sex organs to produce daughter cells with only one-half the number of chromosomes as their parent cells? There are, at the present, no clear and conclusive answers. Will there ever be?

A question of great interest to biologists is, What causes cells to *stop* dividing? To put it differently, Why do organs in a growing animal reach only a set, a fixed, size? Ultimately the answer is related to the types of genes it possesses. But the mechanism is unknown.

The answer to the last mentioned problem is really of tremendous practical importance. Cancer is a condition of uncontrolled cell division in an animal or human body. If biologists knew what restricted mitosis (division and multiplication) in normal tissues, it is entirely probable that they would then discover why cancer cells grow unchecked. This discovery would be a big step forward. Effective curative means might be found to control cancer growths. All humanity would welcome such an eventuality. But so far *this* problem too remains unsolved, and its solution remains known only to God for reasons that we can only guess at.

Related to problems of cell division are those having to do with the mechanism of differentiation, by which simple unspecialized cells become differentiated into a multitude of highly specialized types. Everyone is aware of the variety of tissues in his body. Each of these tissues is composed of specialized cells. For example, in its cytoplasm a muscle cell has many thin filaments arranged in parallel, overlapping fashion. These filaments are thought to allow for contraction and relaxation as they slide across one another. Nerve cells, through their long extensions (axons and dendrites), permit the conduction of electrochemical signals from one point of the body to another. Certain blood cells contain large quantities of a respiratory pigment, hemoglobin, whose molecules bind oxygen and carry it to the various tissues for utilization in the production of energy (ATP).

But the process of differentiation does not always run smoothly. Remember that the process of mitosis yields

123]

daughter cells of equal genetic (DNA) composition. The fertilized egg divides just as any other growing cell does. After the first cleavage there are two cells, then four, eight, sixteen, and so forth. All daughter cells are genetically identical. Therefore, all have equal capabilities and the potential of developing into any of the many specialized types of cells found in the adult. But biologists in their research and experiments in laboratories find that as progressively older nuclei are used for development, more and more malformed embryos result. The inference tentatively drawn from this is that as embryonic nuclei mature, they somehow lose their ability to develop into all types of cells.

Two unsolved problems present themselves: Why do the nuclei lose their earlier developmental potential? How do all the specialized cell types arise from a single primordial cell?

As for the first problem, remember that it is the genes which are thought to control all activities in the cell, and all the nuclei in growing embryos have *identical* genes! Upon division, however, daughter cells do *not* receive the same *cytoplasmic* inheritance. It is now thought that the environment of a nucleus—that is, the cytoplasm—can affect the action of its genes at various stages of development. But the detailed mechanism by which this occurs is not yet understood, and the respective roles of nucleus and cytoplasm in development are an important matter for research.

As for the second problem, we are unable at this stage to account for or explain the mystery of differentiation—how simple original cells can produce a vast number of highly specialized types. All that the best minds among the biologists have been able to do is to make a number of shrewd but unsatisfactory guesses.

We have seen that although it is very small, the cell is an amazingly complex structure. It has the capacity to multiply in an exact manner to bring about tissue growth and repair. In embryological development simple unspecialized cells differentiate to form a great variety of highly specialized types. Among many other functions, these provide for support, movement, coordination, memory, and oxygen supply for other cells. The instructions for doing all these things are contained in the nuclear DNA of a single cell, the fertilized egg.

The knowledge that man has gained about cellular structure and function bears witness to a Designer who is responsible for such incredible complexity. The great problems remaining to be solved (only a few of which we have looked at here) further indicate God's greatness. If man, with his highly sophisticated instruments, his skill in experimentation, and his great capacity for solving complex problems has been able to gain understanding of the cell only at such a slow and wearisome pace—and gain a decidedly imperfect understanding at that—how masterly and superhumanly brilliant a Designer must be to be responsible for its existence!

As a Christian, I look at the cell and exclaim with David: "Great is the Lord, and greatly to be praised; and his greatness is unsearchable." (Ps. 145:3, AV)

THE WONDROUS WORLD
OF HEAT AND ENERGY

BY O. CARROLL KARKALITS

CHEMICAL ENGINEER

Dr. Karkalits is a man of ample education and one who has filled numerous responsible positions. With a B.Sc. degree from Rice Institute and an M.Sc. and a Ph.D. from the University of Michigan he entered on a career of chemical engineering. He was a research chemist with the Shell Oil Company and thereafter was on the chemical engineering staff of the University of Michigan. Still later he became the group leader, Process Development, of the American Cyanamid Company. Presently he is the director of research at Petro-Tex Chemical Corporation, in Texas, a position he has held for several years. He is a member of the American Institute of Chemical Engineers and is a specialist in chemical engineering catalysis.

THERMODYNAMICS describes indeed a wondrous world—that of heat and energy. The term denotes the changing of heat into mechanical work or action, and the converse. Thermodynamics is a science in its own right, and chemists, physicists, and engineers have collaborated in the last two centuries to formulate the laws which are the basis for this science.

Perhaps the most familiar of the laws of thermodynamics is the first law, which states that cosmic energy is *constant*, that it can be neither created nor destroyed. This principle of the conservation of energy was not derived by abstract reasoning but is the result of universal experience. We have yet to find an exception to it in any field of scientific endeavor.

A second basic principle, less well known to the layman than the first law, has to do with the *availability* of energy. Any thinking person is aware of the fact that water will not flow uphill of its own accord; work must be done to pump it to a higher elevation. In an analogous way we can generalize this fact to formulate the second law of thermodynamics. It may be expressed by saying that energy will flow spontaneously from a higher potential to a lower potential, but work must be done to transfer a quantity of energy from a lower potential to a higher potential.

A simple example of the application of the second law is the operation of a household refrigerator. It is well known that heat can be transferred spontaneously from a hot object to a colder object, raising the temperature of the latter, while decreasing the temperature of the former. If a hot brick is placed in a pan of cold water, the temperature of the water will be increased with time, while the temperature of the brick decreases, until eventually they both have the same temperature. This will happen spontaneously, without requiring any other source of energy to make this process go to substantial equilibrium. In order to take heat from the cooler water and transfer it to the hot brick, expenditure of work energy is required from some outside source. This universal experience is the basis of the second law of thermodynamics. In the household refrigerator heat energy is taken from the food products at some relatively low temperature and with the expenditure of work energy is transferred to a radiator coil at some higher temperature. This is a practical application of the second law of thermodynamics.

A corollary of this law, sometimes referred to as the law of entropy (law of unavailable energy), is that any transformation of energy from one form to another in a practical system involves some by-product formation of heat energy. A common example is the heating up of an electric motor during operation. The electric motor is designed to convert electrical energy into mechanical energy. A good portion of the electrical energy, but not all of it, is so converted. There is some friction in the moving parts, which results in heat being liberated from them. The mere passage of the electric current through the windings in the coils of the motor causes also the coils to heat up; this means that energy is lost from the motor in the form of heat.

The second law is sometimes referred to as the law of the degradation of energy (reduction of energy for mechanical work). This manner of speaking arose from our experience that the expenditure of energy to do any kind of work useful to man lowers its availability permanently. We shall have further comment on this presently.

Let it be said at this point that thermodynamics is a very useful and practical science. The chemist can use it, for example, to determine the theoretical extent to which a chemical reaction will proceed. He may not be successful in achieving this degree of completeness, but he knows that thermodynamics has fixed the maximum extent beyond which he cannot expect the reaction to proceed. A mechanical engineer uses thermodynamics, for example, to determine the maximum useful work he can expect to realize from a heat engine working under prescribed operating conditions. Practicing scientists find thermodynamics very useful in defining limits when they attempt to analyze the problems that face them daily. They probably have different interests when they apply thermodynamics, but the underlying principles are the same.

All this is rather abstract and abstruse for the general reader. After these groundbreaking and introductory explanatory remarks let us face certain subjects that concern us all.

There is religion. Thermodynamics and religion—have

they anything in common? More specifically, do thermo-dynamics and theism have an interrelationship of some kind?

Theism is a philosophical concept which traditionally has been developed along the lines of both direct revelation by a Supreme Being (*i.e.*, the Bible) and indirect revelation in the world of nature. The revelation in nature does not lead all men to a common conclusion that there is a Divine Being. The reasons for this are many and varied, and a re-cital of them lies outside the scope of this writing. In the opinion of this writer it is reasonable to believe that the pat-tern of natural phenomena is consistent with belief in a Su-preme Being. The God that the Bible tells us about is one God, and He is the sole Creator of all the cosmos. Not only did He bring the cosmos into being out of nothing, but He sustains it at all times. The Bible does not present a deistic conception of God—one who created the cosmos and then left it alone. The theistic position, based on Bible revela-tion, is one of a Supreme Being who is constantly active in His creation. The very terminology used to describe God in the Hebrew language implies that He is a Being of abso-lutely unlimited energy. He is described as existing inde-pendently of the cosmos, and for that reason pantheistic notions also are foreign to the biblical account.

Both the first and the second laws of thermodynamics are consistent with the theistic conception of the universe pre-sented in the Bible. The first law tells us that the energy of the cosmos is *constant*. It should be remembered that mat-ter and energy are interconvertible (interchangeable) and that matter is a special manifestation of energy. This is con-sistent with the biblical picture of God creating the cosmos and establishing its laws in a definite and specific manner. The reality of the second law is equally impressive. When-ever scientists have been able to devise experiments to check it, the second law also has been universally found to be valid.

But this implies that the universe is running down. By

this we mean that various forms of energy are becoming increasingly unavailable. The earth is dependent on the sun for most of its energy. The energy of the sun is primarily the result of nuclear reactions (akin to those of the hydrogen bomb) going on down in the depths of this star. There are a vast number of similar stars in our galaxy and also in all the other galaxies. These stars are pouring out radiant energy in tremendous quantities, and this cannot continue endlessly. Eventually, in the usual course of events, our sun will die, and the earth will be too cold to support life. This also implies that our sun and all suns had a beginning. Their energy, according to the second law, could never have been unlimited; the process of degradation (reduction of energy) has been a continuous one. Energy was much more available in the past than it is today. To put it in another way, a consequence of the workings of the second law of thermodynamics is that entropy (unavailability of energy) is increasing throughout the universe.

Both biblical theism and thermodynamics therefore point to a creation date for the cosmos. Both also point to the fact that the Supreme Being is not synonymous, or identical, with nature. Thermodynamics excludes the concept of pantheism. God and nature are not the same, and with God there is no diminution of energy or anything else. True, metaphysical judgments lie outside the scope of science. The very term "metaphysics" means "beyond physics," implying that its domain lies beyond that of well-developed physical science. But metaphysical positions concerning God and nature that are reasonable are bound to be in agreement with the dependable findings of physical science.

Besides—here we approach the whole subject from a different angle—the practicing scientist should be a humble man. A study of the history of science, if nothing else, should incline him toward humility. The so-called uncertainty principle of Heisenberg has been a wholesome influence in promoting humility among scientists. The scrap pile of discarded scientific theories is now very large, and it is still growing—a fact that in and by itself should be conducive to humility. This is not an unhealthy situation, for it shows a self-purging characteristic of scientific endeavor. At the same time it points to our definite limitations as scientists. As La Rochefoucauld has aptly said: "It is one of the tragedies of life that many a beautiful theory has been murdered by a brutal gang of facts."

This leads to the obvious conclusion that no scientific theory held today should be considered absolutely final. About thirty years ago, when I first studied chemistry, it was confidently stated that the so-called rare gases (xenon, neon, argon, etc.) were chemically inert and could not be made to combine with other elements. This assertion has been proved false, as any contemporary chemist knows. About the same time the principle of parity in physics was considered to be firmly established. As all physicists know, we recently had to abandon this principle.

This leads us to a fundamental question: Just how firm are the laws of thermodynamics? In view of the foregoing, dogmatism on their firmness and inviolability is unwarranted. As is true of any scientific theory, the future *may* witness their abandonment. It is a thoroughly sound practice, however, to hold onto them until they clearly have been shown to be false.

Some facts, uncovered by science, appear to be so firmly established that it is wholly unlikely they will be shaken by future investigation. The fact that the earth is approximately spherical in shape might be a case in point. I doubt very much that future scientific investigation will disclose it to be a flat disk floating in space. On the other hand, humility, caution, hesitancy, and perhaps suspension of judgment and decision are required in the frontier regions of scientific inquiry where the mass of evidence is not so overwhelming as it is for the shape of the earth. I am not saying that the laws of thermodynamics are as well established and inviolable as the accepted axiom of the shape of the earth. I am saying that the weight of evidence in their favor is im-

131]

pressive and that they are probably more firmly entrenched than many widely held views in physics today. This immense problem is still, after all, a problem. The laws of thermodynamics have not yet been definitely accepted by all reputable scientists with absolute finality.

What are some other problems of thermodynamics? There are, of course, the many problems that arise in the daily application of the science under discussion, many of which frequently seem unsolvable. Among the large problems the overriding one is the application of the thermodynamic laws on a *cosmic* scale. Do these laws operate throughout the cosmos? The fact is that we can only speculate at the present time since no critical observations have been made in the far-distant and unexplored reaches of the universe, countless millions of miles away. There are some physicists among us who frankly question the validity of these laws in the great unknown, and those of us who do no questioning are not in a position to offer positive proof.

Closely allied with this problem is the question of so-called boundary conditions—that is, conditions as they exist in the vast, outlying, unplumbed depths of the universe. Are those peripheral conditions the same as the ones we are familiar with—familiar to an extent? The universe is incalculably vast. The region we have actually explored is smaller, much smaller, than a pinhead compared with an outsized barrel. How can we know that physical conditions in the star galaxies that are fantastic distances away allow the same laws that we observe to function and to function with the same qualitative characteristics? Again there are physicists who profess uncertainty on this score.

In the field of cosmology (study of the orderly processes of nature) one of the speculative theories currently in vogue is the theory of an infinite series of oscillations (swinging movements back and forth, like those of a pendulum). Einstein's special theory of relativity permits a number of possible models of the universe. Two of these models are: (1)

The universe is expanding and will continue to do so forever, and (2) the expansion of the universe is slowing down fairly rapidly and will eventually change to a contraction. If the latter view is true, this will mean that the history of the universe is a series of unending oscillations: continuously expanding, contracting; expanding, contracting. Cosmologists readily point out that in that case we shall have to revise or discard the second law of thermodynamics. This is certainly true.

It amuses this writer that those who hold the infinite oscillations theory (seriously, although tentatively) seem willing to scrap the second law and doubt its application to the cosmos. In almost the same breath, however, they are unwilling to scrap the first law because this is one of their reasons for not accepting a third cosmological theory, known as the steady state theory. Again uncertainty and problems, at least for the physicists here referred to!

The steady state theory just mentioned holds that fresh matter is constantly being created out of nothing in empty space. This matter eventually condenses into galactic systems, which then fill up space between the receding nebulae so that expansion can continue forever. According to this theory, we shall never have a contraction. The basic defect of the steady state theory is that it violates both the first and the second laws of thermodynamics, but we shall not dilate on that here and now.

The entire situation points up the extremely unsettled condition of modern cosmology. Scientists are greatly divided in their opinions, and question marks loom up in almost every direction. The field is prolific indeed in problems great and small.

As for myself, I go along with one of the cosmologists who says that the first law has withstood all the revolutions in physics in the last sixty years and that the majority of physicists would be prepared to give it up only if the most compelling reasons were presented. I would add that the same holds true of the second law. Those of us who have worked with thermodynamics fairly closely are more inclined to discard theories that are not consistent with it than some others who rarely use thermodynamics in their daily work. Whereas dogmatism should be avoided, common sense compels us to continue to accept the laws under discussion until experimental or observational evidence shows that they are no longer valid.

These and other laws of nature, insofar as we have discovered them, are consistent with the theistic conception of reality. All scientific disciplines, including thermodynamics, point to a *rational* pattern in nature. There could not be a rational pattern without a rational Originator.

The belief in a personal God who created the universe and who keeps undergirding it with His might and protecting it with His beneficent care satisfies me both as a man and as a practicing scientist. Back of this world of thermodynamics, this "wondrous world of heat and energy," this world so largely unknown and beset with problems, stands God its Maker. Of that I am sure, and the comfort of this certainty is more than considerable.

CHANGES IN ENERGY—A REAL SOURCE OF PROBLEMS

BY DEAN OWEN HARPER

CHEMICAL ENGINEER

The author of this chapter has years of research and investigation behind him in the field of chemical engineering. He was graduated from Purdue University with B.Sc. and M.Sc. degrees in that science. Further extensive studies in the engineering line were pursued at the University of Cincinnati. For a time he was engineer for Thiokol Chemical Corporation at the Redstone Arsenal, in Huntsville, Alabama. Presently Professor Harper is on the staff of the Department of Chemical Engineering at West Virginia University. He is a member of several professional and honorary societies and is very active in practical Christian work. A temporary illness made the preparation of this chapter difficult, but we are thankful to have the professor in our ranks.

ALL scientific events are manifested by changes in matter and energy. When water freezes to ice, a change in the state of matter occurs: A liquid state turns into a solid state. When water boils to steam, the change in state is from liquid to gas. Changes in energy accompany these transitions of state. Even the warming of water, a process in which no change of state occurs, involves a change in energy. And the loss of energy in falling water can be con-

135]

verted into work, even though the temperature may remain constant. All physical events involve changes in some form of energy.

Chemical reactions change matter in the form of the arrangements and collections of atoms, such as hydrogen and oxygen's combining to form water and hydrogen and nitrogen's reacting to form ammonia. These processes involve changes in energy. Indeed, all chemical reactions involve changes in energy.

Few of us need to be reminded that nuclear reactions are tremendous changes in both matter and energy. The equivalence (equality of value or force) of these two manifestations of nature in the Einstein equation $E = mc^2$ is probably the most widely known relationship in science, and the result of such a reaction is one of the most widely feared phenomena in the world. All nuclear reactions, too, involve changes in energy.

Thermodynamics is the branch of science in which we have formulated generalizations of our experiences with changes in energy. These generalizations, when they are correct and valid, find application in all areas of science. That they find general application attests the unity and harmony of God's creative work. God created the cosmos and established all the cosmic laws, so there is bound to be unity and harmony. The Prophet Jeremiah refers to this in a very touching passage (Ch. 31:35, 36 AV) and many other Bible passages dwell on it.

But the unity and harmony that we have just mentioned are not always evident among scientists when they come to determine and explain the formulated generalizations. Usually these generalizations are referred to as formulations. A formulation is a systematized statement of one's views. In thermodynamics there is a considerable variety of such formulations; this of course, indicates a lack of definite and universally accepted knowledge. A diversity of opinion among scientists means problematic situations— means problems, unsolved problems.

Let us enumerate a number of such problematic situations. We shall number them, to make it easier for the reader.

1. There is equilibrium thermodynamics, which describes processes whose initial and final states are equilibrium states. There is also nonequilibrium thermodynamics, which describes processes as they begin, pass through, and end in nonequilibrium states. Both these branches of thermodynamics have been formulated in several different ways. There are different definitions and assumptions, and both branches are trying to maintain logical consistency.

2. In the classical approach to equilibrium thermodynamics nothing is said about the structure of matter, and the concepts involved must be defined in terms of our common experience. Temperature is often the first such concept that must be defined. Then it is found that physiological responses to hot and cold are not sufficiently accurate for scientific work since a block of wood and a bar of steel at the same temperature produce different sensations. No attempt is made to add to this operational definition.

3. The so-called first law of thermodynamics seeks to give a definition of energy function. It defines energy as a property of matter in terms of heat and work. Others say (and I agree with them) that this is a mistaken definition, that both heat and work are associated only with processes—namely, changes in energy. There has been much argument about this. This may sound like a purely theoretical question, but it really is a question that goes to the heart of the matter and deals with the how and why in thermodynamics. For many, this question is still a problem.

4. In late years a new formulation, called the topological formulation, has been offered of classical thermodynamics, and its adherents are rather numerous. Its leading proponent, P. T. Landsberg, instead of appealing to the familiarity of the fundamental concepts taken from everyday life, maintains that "thermodynamics is among the most

137]

abstract branches of science," and he proceeds with a complicated philosophy of definitions that ordinary mortals cannot follow and that only professionals can appraise and judge. The practical upshot has been a multiplication of uncertainties and problems so far as a clear understanding of thermodynamics is concerned.

5. It is usually stated, and irrevocably, that energy cannot flow from a lower to a higher temperature. Of late it has been asserted that there may be exceptions to this rule, and some examples have been adduced. Whether these hold water is a matter of debate.

6. Many attempts have been made to unify equilibrium and nonequilibrium thermodynamics, but scientists have not yet succeeded to the point where all professionals say Yea and Amen. One leading scientist (J. N. Brønsted) has advanced the theory of energetics, which would replace what are called the first and second laws by two entirely new principles. This would mean somewhat of a revolution in thermodynamic thinking. For the time being most of what this new proposal does is create new problems.

7. Champions of the first law of thermodynamics say that the energy of the universe is constant. Those of the second law say that each process within the universe changes some of the available energy into unavailability, or loss. Entropy describes and measures this loss of available energy. Many scientists believe that heat and energy are constantly being lost and that finally, when heat and energy have reached zero point, the universe must of necessity come to an end. Other scientists are beginning to believe that entropy can be decreased—that the universe can be saved! They do extensive theorizing in this connection. The entropy question, of course, involves a tremendous problem, even though it is not of immediate concern. In my opinion the application of these ideas, pro and con, to the universe is conjecture. Man does not yet know what the entire universe is like. Our descriptions and generalizations are limited to our observations.

8. As is generally known, Einstein formulated the theories of both special and general relativity. Attempts have been made by specialists in thermodynamics to apply Einstein's conceptions to the subject we now have under discussion, and several new thoughts have been developed. But these thoughts are again leading to a variety of enigmas of a complex and highly technical sort. As of today, discussions of relativistic thermodynamics, instead of leading us to the long-looked-for open spaces with the blue heaven overhead, have ushered us still further into the dense, dark, and labyrinthian woods. R. C. Tolman, the leader in this new study, speaks of "the temerity of the human mind in attempting to solve these problems." (*Relativity, Thermodynamics and Cosmology*, London, Oxford University Press, 1934)

9. Since the entropy of processes always increases and since these processes consume time, it is inferred that the direction of time is now positive. Such is the conclusion of Hans Reichenbach, the noted philosopher of science. But the direction of time can only be determined from our observations. There may well be portions of the universe (unobserved) in which the entropy is decreasing, and the direction of time in such localities would be negative. P. W. Bridgman, a specialist in thermodynamics, objects to these views. He states that the notion of time is a primitive concept which cannot be analyzed and which can only be accepted, so that it is meaningless to speak of a reversal of its direction.

And there you are! It has been observed that the study of thermodynamics is far from complete. As a matter of fact, the variety of concepts, definitions, and mathematical tools employed to describe the energy relationships of processes on earth is truly amazing. Glory be to God who created this world—its behavior consistent, its description highly elusive.

The British scientist Tolman, whom we have just quoted,

says in the same volume, "It is appropriate to approach the problems of cosmology with feelings of respect for their importance and of awe for their vastness." He is, of course, entirely right. Too many of us have in these recent years, with their multitude of technological inventions, become "vain in [our] imaginations" (Rom. 1:21, AV) and have actually come to believe that it is only a matter of time before human knowledge, also that of cosmology and thermodynamics, will have become full-orbed, perfect. They assume that there are no limits to the potentialities of the present human mind.

But there are limits, all right! As a student of thermodynamics, I am all in favor of searching and researching in my particular field, but I also recognize human limits. Yet this does not put a damper on my work. I study and investigate and seek to trace the thoughts of my Creator-God, so that I may magnify Him all the more and help benefit humanity, and at the same time I am greatly inspired by the thought to which the Apostle Paul gave permanent form:

"For we know in part, and we prophesy in part. But when that which is perfect is come, then that which is in part shall be done away. When I was a child, I spake as a child, I understood as a child, I thought as a child: but when I became a man, I put away childish things. For now we see through a glass (the very imperfect mirror of that age) darkly; but then face to face: now I know in part; but then shall I know even as also I am known. (I Cor. 13:9-12, AV)

According to the general teaching of Scripture, this present "knowing in part" applies to both our spiritual and natural state. For a scientist who has faith in God this is wonderful information. In all his mental struggles he can say to himself, "What a future lies before me!"

THE ANSWER TO ASTRONOMY'S FINAL ENIGMA

BY FREDERICK H. GILES, JR.

PHYSICIST

ASTRONOMER

The following chapter came to us from ancient Mesopotamia (Iraq), where Dr. Giles was invited to serve as Fulbright Lecturer in Physics at the University of Baghdad. Dr. Giles' regular position is a professorship in physics and astronomy at the University of South Carolina. The professor is known for his keen thinking, expert scholarship —and delightful wit. He was graduated from Wheaton College, Illinois, with a B.Sc. in physics (with high honors), and thereafter acquired a Ph.D. in physics from the University of Illinois. After a professorship at Bowling Green State University, Ohio, he went, in 1957, to the University of South Carolina, where physics again was his forte and astronomy continued to be a subject of intense study, one in which today he is exceptionally well versed. By appointment of the American Physical Society, Dr. Giles is the Regional Counsellor in Physics for South Carolina. He is a specialist in chemical and biological physics, as well as in electrolysis, and belongs to numerous distinguished scientific organizations.

ALTHOUGH modern astronomy was probably conceived when man first took cognizance of his environment and then gestated for the centuries during which he has viewed and speculated regarding the regularity of day and night, the cycle of the seasons, the phases of the moon, the movement of the planets against the background of fixed stars, and the meaning of it all, it seems fair to state that it was really given birth to in the second half of the seventeenth century with the work of Isaac Newton. His work brought about the shift in thought which elevated observation and experiment to an authoritative position in man's thinking. This shift marks the genesis of all modern science, and astronomy shares this heritage.

Astronomy in particular, however, was "delivered" with the recognition that the laws established in terrestrial laboratories are also applicable to celestial problems. For centuries heavenly bodies were generally considered to be free of the restraints and regulations that govern earthly experience. In his *Law of Universal Gravitation* Newton recognized the force attracting a falling apple to be identical with the force that holds the moon in its path about the earth and that keeps the earth and other planets in their orbits about the sun. Terrestrial and celestial physics were found to be one!

Such acceptance of the true nature of physical laws has been strikingly vindicated. The most famous test of the law of universal gravitation came in 1846, some 120 years after Newton's death. The planet Uranus behaved deviously, whereas all other motions within the solar system had been calculated and described as exactly as could be observed. Either the law of gravitation had to be modified slightly for large distances (Uranus is 1,782,000,000 miles from the sun), or there was some as yet undetected object near the planet that caused the deviations. The validity of the law being assumed, the necessary position of the unseen object was calculated. Upon receiving word, the astronomer Johann Galle almost immediately sighted Neptune—and very close to the predicted location. The planet was discovered on paper before it was found in the heavens!

Today this tenet of astronomy is taken for granted. All astronomical knowledge rests on it. It echoes and shapes the thinking of all of us. Everyone fully expects satellites and rockets in outer space to act according to terrestrial principles. In the most obvious case, because of our experiences with objects here on earth everyone knew there was a back side to the moon, although it was viewed directly (by the Russian satellite Lunik III) only very recently.

Armed with the new knowledge, the astronomers have established their science, and its growth has paralleled the progress in all science and technology. Technological advances have extended observational horizons to almost unbelievable limits. Here are a few of the things the experts say they have learned (I am stating them objectively, am not making comments of my own):

The human eye can detect a star as bright as the sun at a distance of about 100 light-years (a light-year corresponds to a distance of 5,880,000,000,000 miles). With the 200-inch telescope the same type of star could be seen 1,000 times farther away.

Galaxies are tremendous "island universes" in space, each containing a countless number of suns. Our own Milky Way galaxy is but one of apparently billions of galaxies. Distances among them have been estimated at several billion light-years.

The number of stars in the observable universe has risen to approximately 10^{20} (that's a 1, followed by 20 zeros), of which only an insignificant number can be detected with the naked eye. Modern equipment does wonders. The unaided eye can probably recognize two automobile headlights as "two" at a distance of about 4 miles, whereas the 200-inch telescope could theoretically resolve the same two sources at a distance of 4,000 miles.

Astronomers have invented all kinds of experimental techniques (with the kind help of physicists and chemists) or have unashamedly borrowed them from still other sciences as the need or opportunity arose. One of the things borrowed by astronomers is spectroscopy (the science of light spectra), by means of which temperatures are meas-

143]

ured and chemical composition is studied on stellar surfaces. The loan has often been repaid. In 1868 the element helium was spectroscopically identified on the sun, twenty-seven years earlier than it was isolated on the earth.

Light travels as a wave motion, and the wavelength (and therefore the apparent color) will be shifted if the emitting object is approaching or receding. This Doppler shift of light is used to measure stellar and galactic speeds. Relativity, originally developed to resolve some questions in electromagnetic theory, postulates the constancy of the speed of light—the astronomers' yardstick. A light-year is the distance light travels in one year.

Nuclear physicists discovered processes which have been borrowed to elucidate the source of the tremendous amounts of energy emitted by the stars (the sun, an average star, radiates at the rate of 521,000,000,000,000,000,000,000,000 horsepower—I just wanted to see what that number looked like when it was written out).

Visible light is only a tiny part of the electromagnetic spectrum, so astronomers have recently turned their attention to observations of the heavens by means of invisible light. Since World War II, radio astronomy has contributed significantly to the picture of the universe. The Milky Way galaxy, *our* galaxy, is shaped somewhat like a pinwheel, having long spiral arms of stars. The sun is on the inside edge of the third arm, about 27,000 light-years from the center of the galaxy and moving around it at about 150 miles per second.

Atoms make up the stars, stars have been arranged into galaxies, galaxies into clusters, and clusters—they're just in space, endless space. There are countless billions of everything. And the universe is found to be in a state of rapid expansion, with galaxies receding one from the other at unimaginable speed.

This rough and very limited sketch may give some idea of what the experts feel is "known," and it sets the stage for a discussion of the "unknown." But before the unknowns are considered, a few comments are necessary. Brief reflection indicates that there are kinds and levels of ignorance, even as there appear to be kinds and levels of knowledge. The ensuing paragraphs follow an outline stemming from a catalogue of these distinctions, even though the demarcation lines are admittedly fuzzy and fluid. There remain the deeper problems of epistemology (the science of the grounds and methods of knowledge), which I only partially recognize. I respect but cannot emulate those who capably examine such topics as the understanding of understanding, the knowledge of knowledge, and the ignorance of ignorance. Therefore, only the most obvious varieties of unknowns will be pointed up. It is to be hoped that my display of ignorance will be wittingly and provocatively done. I shall try to limit consideration to the unknowns which are shared by the entire community of astronomers and not disclose too much of the store of ignorance which is my personal possession.

First, there is the ignorance of details. This is the evident ignorance of which we are made aware by the logical and factual gaps in the current picture of the universe. It includes the lack of data to decide, check, and substantiate theoretical suggestions, and it contains the undeveloped theory needed properly to describe and orient observations already recorded. This type of unknown is revealed by such questions as: What does the back of the moon look like? Are any of the planets in our solar system habitable? What is the source of the radio noise from Jupiter? What is the mechanism for the exceptionally high temperature of the solar corona? What are the density and distribution of galaxies throughout space? What are the quastars, and how are they able to produce so much energy so fast?

For some of the answers it is simply a matter of the time needed to analyze a backlog of existing data or to obtain new data with available equipment. Experimental improvements will expunge other unknowns. Radio telescopes, with

145]

greater sensitivity and resolution, will extend our horizons and add much more detail to our map of the universe. Space vehicles now under construction will allow observation from above the atmosphere—unrestricted by dust, city lights, shimmer, airglow, and absorption. The moon, the planets, and the sun (our nearest star) will be scrutinized. The whole spectrum of electromagnetic radiation will be available for viewing. The suggestive initial X-ray observations will be extended to determine the nature of their source. Nuclear physicists are working on a neutrino telescope for possible analysis of processes in the interior of the stars. The neutrino is an extremely penetrating and therefore frightfully elusive (it usually goes straight through the devices used to detect it!) particle which is produced in nuclear reactions. With information which appears to be forthcoming, soon cosmologists should be able to eliminate some models—some guesses on the underlying nature and overall structure—of the universe which now are vying for acceptance on the basis more of philosophical inclination than of observational pressure.

It is now necessary to point out another tenet of astronomical faith, which has already been implied and which underlies both our knowledge and our ignorance. Stated simply, it is: Physical laws are independent of time. This, too, is vindicated faith. For example, the times of past and future eclipses have often been calculated. The entire predictive aspect of modern astronomy and modern science in general rest on this postulate. Really, the faith to extend physical laws over long distances is intimately and inextricably connected with the faith to apply physical laws either forward or backward in time. By virtue of the finite velocity of light, looking out involves looking back. Space and time have been linked in language. Looking out a distance of 6,000,000,000 light-years involves receiving information from the inconceivably distant past. It involves a faith in the delivery system of this information—the light does not get "tired" during 6,000,000,000 light-years of travel! Certainly, an audacious but fundamental tenet!

On this basis, it becomes apparent that the picture previously described is not static. Change, motion, and changes of motion mark the observations at all levels. Fascinating questions arise. In the earth-moon combination tidal friction tends to slow down the system, and the moon moves away from the earth. How long has this been going on? How close could the moon have been to the earth at some time in the distant past? The sun, like a tremendous furnace, is burning nuclear fuel and emitting energy at a rate previously quoted. How long has this been going on? How long can it be expected to continue? How did it start? What of the "ashes"? The distant galaxies appear to be receding, with the most distant ones moving away the fastest. What are they moving from? What are they moving toward? Do such questions have any meaning—perhaps a vital meaning?

More detailed discussion of these problems will probably be found in the chapters accompanying this one. The questions raised illustrate a second sort of ignorance, which is also evident and recognized but which has an "unavoidableness" about it. It is the ignorance of origins. Aside from biblical revelation, from a purely scientific viewpoint origins are by their very nature unobservable. But one may argue back from observed consequences, then argue forward again from the resulting conclusions, and then observationally verify (or not verify) the final predictions. In this manner the origin of the moon is being examined, as well as the origin of the solar system. The origin of the solar system is likely associated with the origin of the sun itself, so the question of stellar formation and the possibility of other planetary systems are being studied. Stars gather into galaxies for some reason not well understood. The shapes, the motions (within and without), and the clustering tendency of these galaxies are recognized, but their origins are not predictable as the necessary consequence of any current theory. All this falls under ignorance of origins so far as present-day "pure" science is concerned.

So, employing the techniques of mathematics and the physical sciences, astronomers seek to extend their understanding in both distance and time. Their goal is to acquire a comprehensive knowledge of the structure and activities of the universe and its myriad parts. No one dares say when or how this goal may be reached. When new understanding is gained, it is inevitably accompanied by a new realization of ignorance. New knowledge reveals new unknowns. Close scrutiny tends to expose more detail, necessitating still closer scrutiny. Research in astronomy can be expected to fill gaps in our present picture of the universe; it can be expected to extend that picture in both time and space; but past experience indicates that it can be expected to disrupt the picture as well.

These comments expose another sort of ignorance—a kind of ignorance of "thin ice"—which is not evident but of which we are profoundly aware. New data, ideas, and insights often uncover deficiencies in our descriptions of the universe and result in breakthroughs which open nascent (newborn) or dormant (inactive) regions of experience to the light of thought and experiment. Improved precision of observation and measurement may render currently correct theories unable to cope with the new facts. Newton's *Law of Universal Gravitation* appeared to explain perfectly the motions of the planets in our solar system until precision measurements of the precession rate (rate of change in the direction of the axis of a rotating body) of the planet Mercury revealed an inexplicable difference between calculation and observation. The discrepancy amounted to about forty-three seconds of arc per century—exceedingly small, but sufficient to be accurately measured and sufficient to indicate that Newton's law was not entirely adequate. One of the early victories of the theory of general relativity was the accurate calculation of this precession. Newton's law can be considered only a good approximation of the actual state of affairs.

A new insight may cause disruption. Less than fifteen years ago, following a study of star populations and a recognition of more than one group of a particular sort of variable star, estimates of intergalactic distances increased by a factor of ten. The universe grew ten times by virtue of a bright idea! During the early 1940's the prevalent hypothesis regarding the formation of the solar system pictured the planets as having been torn out of the sun during a chance collision with an external celestial object. Astronomers rejected the idea of planets produced spontaneously during the formation of the sun since "in view of our present knowledge this attractive and simple hypothesis will not stand up under serious criticism." By the late 1940's, however, owing to a clever insight, the idea that would "not stand up under serious criticism" became the prevailing one.

Breakthroughs generally occur abruptly—and often embarrassingly! The quotation in the previous paragraph is a properly guarded statement by a reliable author. It reflected the state of knowledge at the time of writing. Unfortunately many authors have been careless in their statements; they have announced definite knowns which became unknowns. Recently, in a review of the second edition of a well-known book on astronomy, the reviewer listed more than ten theories and numerical values which appeared as "undoubted" ten years earlier in edition one and which are again described as "undoubted," *but completely different,* in edition two! Scrupulous modern authors of astronomical material strive to maintain a balanced skepticism which is properly wary of "established facts," as well as on the alert in cases of obvious ignorance.

Ignorance of the "thin ice" type is closely akin to ignorance of fundamentals—the ignorance that becomes strikingly evident when previously reliable laws and relationships are pushed into use in situations beyond their recognized

149]

limits of applicability. Mark Twain tweaked the noses of the scientists in his *Life on the Mississippi* on this very point. Twain said:

> In the space of 176 years the Lower Mississippi has short-ened itself 242 miles. This is an average of a trifle over one mile and a third per year. Therefore any calm person, who is not blind or idiotic, can see that in the Oölitic Silurian Period, just a million years ago next November, the Lower Mississippi river was upwards of one million, three hundred thousand miles long, and stuck out over the Gulf of Mexico like a fish-ing rod. . . . There is something fascinating about Science. One gets such wholesale returns of conjecture out of such a trifling investment of fact.

Then there is conjectural ignorance. Currently our faith in the applicability of the earth's established laws stretches out—and back—6,000,000,000 light-years. Recent advances in data and theory indicate that the universe is expanding, and many astronomers feel that space-time is expanding. Ex-trapolating (drawing conclusions by inference) back in time, one finds the peculiar situation of a shrunken universe in which the very concepts of time and space may not be useful in description. Our ignorance at the extremes of the cosmos is reflected in our ignorance at terrestrial levels. What is more, our faith in the unrestricted applicability of our most familiar concepts is being shaken.

With the concepts of space, time, and even of mass in ques-tion, what becomes of our most fundamental ideas? As far as we know, there is only one universe—and how do you de-scribe something of which there is only one? Familiar con-cepts are familiar because they provide explanatory foun-dations in a wide variety of situations. But the universe is not like anything else. Its nature alone must determine the con-cepts necessary to its ultimate description.

All this is conjectural ignorance. The questions of life, of other sentient beings, elsewhere in the universe fall under this same head. Currently estimates of the number of in-habited planets in the observable universe range from one up to billions—with observational data available for only one! Great things are being expected from the neutrino telescope, referred to above. What is now observed, so it is said, is merely a small fluctuation of an underlying, incomprehensively larger energy store.

This should be enough! I do not know where scientific insight ends and pure science fiction begins, and I am not clever enough to come up with much of either. I do know that modern astronomy, in its fascinating quest to understand the universe, is marked by much faith, considerable knowledge, and a sizable pile of ignorance. In saying this, I don't in the least seek to discourage astronomers who are still in the grub stage from seeking fulfillment and substantiation of their dreams. But there is one thing that they—and we all —should remember: When one ponders the nature of the physical universe, one should not stop there. In fact, one cannot stop there. One is forced to a consideration of ultimates, to a consideration of origins and ends, and this is the world of philosophy and religion.

Theories and attitudes in astronomy both determine and reflect the "world views" of men. The prevailing picture of the universe colors, and is colored by, the thinking of an age. The present age is no exception.

Modern astronomy implies much about man himself. He is physically insignificant—a speck on a speck near a speck in a speck. Furthermore, he shares a physical oneness with the rest of the universe: The laws of physics, chemistry, and biology that are at work in him are the same laws that are at work in the rest of the cosmos. Man also displays a striking mental continuity with the universe, while maintaining an almost paradoxical transcendence over it. With pencil and paper he formulates the logical structures of mathematics and then finds the same structures applicable to description of the world around him. This shows that man's transcendence over the universe is partly of a mental nature. Man is intelligent; he has intellectual faculties.

It is by these intellectual faculties that man becomes aware of the enormous and enormously intricate network of design in the universe. This evident fact of design in the universe has often been advanced as a conclusive argument for the existence of God, and although capable scholars have often denied the conclusiveness of the argument, it certainly cannot be denied that the fact of universal design delivers a telling thrust in the direction of God's existence. There is no doubt that the Apostle Paul, a man of great intellect, meant to champion the same thought when he said, in Romans (Ch. 1:20, AV), that "the invisible things of him (God) from the creation of the world are clearly seen, being understood by the things that are made, even his eternal power and Godhead. . . ." Today the God of creation is shown to be much more glorious and awesome: Our picture of His universe has exploded in space, time, and content, so that our concept of His power and majesty becomes overwhelming.

The science of astronomy provides at least one other insight regarding the nature of men. Why should they study the heavens anyway? Why should men care? Yet they do— and always have! Among the most ancient nations astronomy, usually in the form of astrology, captured the imagination of men, made them search, investigate, calculate, and build a hundred and one faiths, beliefs, superstitions, and idol fallacies on it. The awesomeness of the universe inspired fear, a silent and constant alarm. Although intellectual and scientific advances since those ancient or prehistoric days have made mankind in more cultured climes shed much of its distressful burden, fear is still with us in our enlightened age and place—a fear born of modern scientific developments and their undeniable potentialities for dire evil.

For those of us who hold the Christian faith there is the consolation, the heartening knowledge, that He through whom the world was made is also, and will abide forever, its almighty Sovereign and Protector. As the New Testament has it, "God . . . hath in these last days spoken unto us by his Son, whom he hath appointed heir of all things, by whom also he made the worlds; who being the brightness of his glory and the express image of his person, (upholds) all things by the word of his power. . . ." (Heb. 1:1-3, AV) We

[152

trust a God who has revealed himself in the Holy Scriptures, in the Person and work of Jesus Christ in history, and in the inspiring, guiding, and strengthening action of the Holy Spirit in our immediate experience. We trust a God who made and is Master of the cosmos. Here astronomy and Christianity meet. God, for us, is the answer to astronomy's final enigma.

As in the case of the universe, the more one learns about God, the more one finds there is to know. More understanding of God is inevitably accompanied by the realization of more widespread and deeper ignorance. It is humbling to realize that the best astronomers recognize their limited knowledge most keenly, and it is the oldest and wisest of saints who most keenly feel their limited knowledge of God. It was the brilliant Apostle Paul who reminded his readers that "now we see through a glass, darkly." (I Cor. 13:12, AV)

God is certainly no less complex and many-faceted than His universe. Christians share with the astronomer the problem of contemplating and describing the unique in terms of more familiar concepts. One rather nasty problem not shared by astronomers is that of consumer expectation—no one seems to expect to know all about astronomy after a single course in college. Yet I am continually amazed at those who expect God to be somehow less intricate and awesome than the universe and who demand complete answers to all questions regarding God during an hour's lecture, in the course of an evening's bull session, or, even worse, from their elementary Sunday-school teacher.

This seems to be a good place to stop. Ignorance in astronomy is recognized, and far from being a discouragement, it serves as an impetus for further study and observation. Ignorance regarding God is also admitted and recognized, but again, far from being the cause of dejection or rejection, it should provide reason for delving deeper and learning more.

It is a rewarding challenge to be working to unravel the intricacies of the universe. It is a fascinating experience to be attempting to learn more of the Person and providence of God. It is an exciting adventure to be doing both.

153]

STARS OF LIGHT AND PROBLEMS
OF GREAT DARKNESS

BY H. HAROLD HARTZLER

MATHEMATICIAN

ASTRONOMER

Dr. Hartzler is widely known and respected in academic circles. He is personally known to many hundreds of American scientists because of his active and dedicated service to fellow scientists in his official capacities. After being graduated from Juniata College, he attended Rutgers University and obtained a Ph.D. degree in physics. He did postgraduate work at Pennsylvania State University, the University of Michigan, and the University of Arizona, where he specialized in astronomy. For several years he was a professor of Mathematics at Goshen College and thereafter, since 1958, has been a professor at Mankato State College, in Minnesota, filling the chair first of physics and presently of mathematics and astronomy. Dr. Hartzler has been secretary-treasurer of the American Scientific Affiliation, its president, and for the last several years its executive secretary, a national position of great influence. He holds memberships in fourteen state and national scientific organizations.

AFTER four failures the Russians have succeeded just recently in making a soft landing on the moon with their collection of scientific instruments. We Americans plan to catch up with them very shortly. Already we have snapped some fairly close pictures of the silvery orb, but since the cameras were still several thousand miles away from their object, the pictures were indistinct and hazy.

It's all somewhat ironical. The world's top-ranking astronomers (many of them, at least) seem to know a great deal about star clusters billions of miles away; cosmographers and astrophysicists in many different countries have informed us about enormous solar systems at the same or a far greater distance; we have aeronautical engineers whose know-how is unprecedented, amazing. But the moon, a mere 238,000 miles away and almost a next-door neighbor in an obliquely upward direction, is still out of reach, and much of our knowledge about it is guesswork.

I think we would do well to limit our remarks in this chapter to certain things that we are fairly sure of and certain other things that we are entirely sure of and to do so in plain, nontechnical language. I have mentioned the moon; let us take a very brief look at it.

A Few Facts About the Moon

The moon, at an average distance of 238,000 miles, is our nearest neighbor in space. Owing to the fact that its orbit around the earth is elliptical, rather than circular, and owing to the gravitational attraction of the sun, its distance varies from about 222,000 miles to about 253,000 miles. The moon is 2,160 miles in diameter, and its mass (quantity of matter) is one-eightieth that of the earth. The force of gravity on its surface is one-sixth that on the earth; this means that a person weighing 180 pounds on the earth would weigh only 30 pounds on the moon. This low value of gravity will lead to some highly interesting experiences when man finally lands on the moon—if he ever does.

Because of its relative proximity many things are known about the moon. But a great many other things are still mysteries. We do not know, for example, what kinds of materials exist on the surface of the moon. The albedo, or reflecting power, of the moon is low, amounting to about 0.07. This means that the moon reflects only about 7 percent of the light that shines on it. During an eclipse of the moon there is a very rapid loss of heat, showing that the high temperature of the surface under full sunlight is confined to a thin surface layer. Such facts as these lead scientists to postulate that the surface consists of a layer of dust. How deep this layer is remains a subject of dispute among different astronomers.

It is well established that the moon has very little atmosphere. Both the fact that there is no change in brightness between the center and the edge and the fact that stars are very suddenly occulted (eclipsed) by the moon tend to support the theory of a very thin atmosphere on the moon. Such observations, however, do not rule out the possibility, suggested by some, that the moon may have an atmosphere something like one ten-thousandth of the density of the earth's atmosphere. But nothing has been established; no reliable statistics of any kind are available.

Five types of lunar topography (physical features of the moon) may be observed with the aid of a telescope. These are seas, or maria; mountains; craters; rays (whitish lines seen on the moon); and rills, or clefts (long narrow valleys). The seas are a misnomer since there can be very little water on the moon. They simply consist of large, smooth, relatively dark areas. These are surrounded by mountains of considerable height. Some of these areas, however, are so vast that an observer standing in the center would be unable to see the mountains since they would lie beyond his horizon.

The craters are formations which have the appearance of volcanic craters on the earth. Many thousands of such craters are found on the moon. They vary in size from small pits to large ones like Copernicus, which has a diameter of 56 miles, or Clarius, with a diameter of 140 miles. In many cases there are secondary craters in the floor of the main formation; in other cases a peak or group of peaks rises from the floor. The big question here concerns the cause of the craters.

Two theories have been proposed. One assumes that they are the result of meteorites striking the lunar surface. To explain the large number of craters would require the moon to have been hit by very many large meteorites. If this be the case, the question may well be asked why there is little evidence that the earth also has been struck by many large meteorites.

The second theory assumes that at some distant time the moon was a hot molten mass. After considerable cooling, the action of great volcanoes may have built up the many lunar craters, or heated gases from the interior may have burst through the crust as great bubbles with the resultant formation of craters. It is impossible to decide which of the two theories is correct or if both of them are wrong. The problem is unsolved.

Many people believe that the moon has a profound effect on the weather here on earth and that the growth of plants depends on the phase of the moon at the time of planting. Extensive research over long periods of time has failed to show that such beliefs have any validity. But the moon does have one very important effect on the earth, and that concerns the formation of the tides. There can be little doubt that the gravitational effect of the moon is the principal cause of the tides. The sun also has attracting power and affects the oceans and connected gulfs, bays, and rivers, but the gravitational pull of the moon is three times as strong as the sun's. So our seamen are subject daily to the action of the moon as it acts unequally on the waters in different parts of the earth and disturbs their equilibrium, thus causing the familiar ebb and flow.

The Apostle Paul speaks of the "glory of the moon" (I Cor. 15:41, AV), and the soft, mellow moonlight has through the ages been a blessing from God. Moonlight, of course, is really sunlight come to us indirectly, by reflection. The moon's glory, of which the Apostle wrote, is reflected glory, but with a distinctive beauty all its own.

That Well-known Star—Our Sun

The most obvious astronomical object observed by man is the sun. This celestial body seems to move around the earth every day. We continue to speak of sunrise and sunset. But

157]

all well-informed persons know that it is the turning of the earth on its axis which accounts for the apparent rising and setting of the sun. The sacred writer, in Psalm 19, adjusted himself to the popular conception when he described the sun in beautiful poetic language and said, "The sun . . . is as a bridegroom coming out of his chamber, and rejoiceth as a strong man to run a race." (Ps. 19:4, 5, AV)

Astronomically the sun is simply an average star. Although it may appear to us as a rather small object in the sky, not much larger than the moon, it is known to be tremendous in size. Its diameter is 865,000 miles. Imagine the sun as a hollow sphere, with the earth placed at its center. Then the moon, placed at its present distance from the earth, would be only a little more than halfway from the center of the sun to its surface. The sun's total volume (space occupied) is about 1,300,000 times the volume of the earth. The mass (quantity of matter) of the sun is approximately 330,000 times the earth's mass. Thus, its density is one-fourth that of the earth or about 1.4 times the density of water. Whereas the force of gravity on the surface of the moon is only one-sixth of that on the earth, calculation shows that on the sun's surface the force of gravity is nearly 28 times that on the earth. Thus, a mass weighing 220 pounds here on earth would have a weight of more than 3 tons when transported to the surface of the sun.

The temperature on the surface of the sun has been determined to be about 9,600° F. This seems a fantastic temperature compared with the highest temperature of a body here on earth. It means that the material composing the sun must be in a gaseous state, for no solid or liquid could exist at such a temperature.

The sun furnishes practically all the energy received by the earth. We receive, on the average, 1.94 calories per square centimeter every minute. Every square yard of the sun's surface is radiating energy at the rate of 70,000 horsepower. The total energy generated by the sun is so enormous that it would be sufficient to melt a layer of ice 40 feet thick over its entire surface in one minute.

A number of theories have been proposed to account for this enormous and constant output of energy from the sun. The sun is too hot for chemical combinations to take place. Therefore, ordinary burning can hardly be considered the source of the sun's energy. Furthermore, if the sun's mass were composed of pure carbon and this were burned, it would last only a comparatively short time. A century ago it was thought that the energy came from a gradual decrease in its volume. This is known as the gravitational-collapse theory. The theory held in repute today assumes that hydrogen atoms are transformed into helium atoms with a consequent loss of mass, which is converted into energy according to Einstein's equation ($E = mc^2$). The enormity of this energy release is revealed by the fact that the conversion of 2.2 pounds of mass into energy would be equivalent to the energy produced by the burning of 3,000,000 tons of coal and is comparable to the total amount of electric power produced in the United States in a month.

But just what is taking place in the sun to *cause* this very large energy output? This is another of the many unknowns in astronomy. Man is again facing unsolved problems. Personally I am thankful and glad that an all-knowing and almighty God is in charge of things. Oftentimes, these days, people are afraid of the possible results of accidental atomic explosions or other great destructive happenings. What would our situation be like if Almighty God were not in firm control of the enormous forces of the sun or those of the other countless celestial bodies?

Ever since the time of Galileo many observations of sunspots have been made. They require the use of a telescope, together with some other equipment. The spots are comparatively cool regions where enormous cyclonic whirls take place in the atmosphere of the sun. Their number, size, and duration vary greatly. On some days no spots are visible, while on other occasions there appear to be several hundred. Some are quite small, just visible in the telescope, while others are large, at least ten times the diameter of the earth. When the spots are observed over a long period of time, it is found that there is a definite periodicity connected with their number. A maximum number of spots occurs about every eleven years. Another phenomenon connected with sunspots is that each of them has an intense magnetic field. Sunspots may be classified according to their properties as unipolar, bipolar, and complex. Unipolar groups of spots exhibit the same magnetic polarity, like one end of a bar magnet. Bipolar groups consist of two spots quite close together and showing opposite polarity. Complex groups are those in which the polarities are irregularly distributed.

Many questions with regard to sunspots remain unanswered. What is their real nature? What are they caused by? Why do they exhibit a periodicity with respect to their number? How does one explain sunspot magnetism? There are many other unanswered questions pertaining to details. They all constitute problems that await solution.

One of the most impressive sights in nature is a total eclipse of the sun. This takes place very infrequently and can be seen only from a particular location on the earth. Furthermore, its duration is short, usually only a few minutes. To the astronomer such an event is very important. Often he travels a long distance to record it by photographic means. There is no longer any mystery connected with an eclipse, either of the sun or of the moon. The explanation is quite simple. As the moon revolves about the earth once each month, it continually casts a long shadow. When this shadow covers a given portion of the earth, there is said to be an eclipse of the sun (the sun is not visible in its clarity in that particular part of the earth). The earth also casts a shadow, and when this covers the moon, we have an eclipse of the moon. To the ancients both events were very mysterious, and in many cases it was thought that an eclipse indicated the displeasure of the gods. In the Bible the Prophet Joel described eclipses of both the sun and the moon in these words: "The sun shall be turned into darkness, and the moon into blood, before the great and the terrible day of the Lord come." (Ch. 2:31, AV) This is a vivid description of a total eclipse of the moon. On such an occasion the moon has a red appearance owing to the fact that the sun's rays are bent as they pass through the atmosphere of the earth and then strike the moon. Most of the blue light is scattered and therefore does not get through. A similar phenomenon is observed in many sunrises and sunsets when the sky appears a brilliant red and often presents a magnificent view.

Some Remarks About Our Solar System and the Universe

Our solar system includes the sun; the nine principal planets, which revolve around the sun; the asteroids, consisting of thousands of relatively small bodies revolving around the sun between the orbits of Mars and Jupiter; and the satellites, which revolve around the planets (including the moon, which revolves around the earth), as well as comets, meteors, dust, and gas whirling and swirling between the planets. Astronomically speaking, the solar system is quite compact. The distance from the sun to the outermost planet is believed to be about 4,000,000,000 miles, while the distance to the nearest star has been estimated to be more than 6,000 times as great. (This humble writer won't guarantee the correctness or even approximate correctness of these figures.)

There are any number of theories about the origin and development of the solar system, from those of Descartes, Buffon, and Kant in the seventeenth and eighteenth centuries to that of Kuiper in very recent years, but they have remained theories (speculations) in a most literal sense. The proponents of the theories have many followers, but there are many others who turn the theories down, one as well as another. The latter argue that practically all the theorists are at variance with one another. They also feel that although the immensity of the solar system and certainly that of the universe in its entirety are established facts, too many recent astronomers seem to vie with one another in adding unwarranted astronomical figures to astronomical facts. One of these enthusiastic ones, for example, estimates that there may be 1,000,000,000 (one billion) solar systems in our own galaxy. Others have proposed the existence of several billion galaxies in the known universe. I prefer not to keep abreast of such runaway imaginations.

The truth of the matter is that astronomers have very little evidence for the existence of any solar system except our own. About our own solar system we know quite a number of things. About what lies outside we know very little. Both these immense regions are thronged with unanswered questions and unsolved problems. Both regions exclaim: "Ah Lord God! behold, thou hast made the heaven and the earth by thy great power and stretched out arm. . . . Thou (art) the Great, the Mighty God . . . Great in counsel (wisdom and knowledge) and mighty in work. . . ." (Jer. 32:17,18, 19, AV)

That is the general answer of Divine revelation to questions pertaining to the universe in its entirety. Specific answers to specific technical questions about the universe are not given in the Bible—but neither does philosophy or science provide them!

How large is the universe?

How many celestial bodies does it contain?

What is its average density?

Does it remain constant in time—*i.e.*, are *all* its laws fixed and invariable?

How long will the sun, as the light and power center of our solar system, continue to function at its present rate?

These and many others are baffling questions, unanswerable questions, for any astronomer or group of astronomers.

Astronomers have explored many details of the physical universe, and we hope they will continue to do so with all zeal and application of heart and mind. We know far more about God's handiwork than we did some generations back and have ever-increasing reasons to join the morning stars (angels) in their creation song (Job 38:7).

But the Astronomer Supreme has evidently kept much basic and detailed information for himself, at least in the present dispensation. Will eternity, after a while, raise the great curtain for us?

WATER VAPOR–A VITAL FACTOR IN ALL LIFE PROCESSES

BY DWIGHT L. RANDALL

METEOROLOGIST

In the present age of space travel and aeronautics the Federal Government leans heavily for dependable information on a limited number of top-rank meteorologists. Dwight L. Randall is one of them. His formal schooling was: a B.Sc. from Tulane University, specialized courses at The Massachusetts Institute of Technology, and an M.Sc. from Georgetown University. For twenty years he was a U.S. weather observer and analyst; then was on the staff of the Air Corps Technical School, U.S. Army; afterward was a physical scientist for the National Bureau of Standards; and thereafter was a physicist for the U.S. Naval Research Laboratory, where he was finally promoted to the position of head of the Radio Meteorological Section, in special charge of the Wave Propagation Branch —his present position. He is a specialist in microwave radio propagation and meteorological instrumentation.

Two men were once crossing a freshly plowed field just after a rain shower. Presumably, both men were looking for agates in the furrows, but one of them had his attention fixed on the sky and the clouds. As he looked into the heavens, he wondered how much water was in the air. It occurred to him that over a large continent there was more water in the form of vapor flowing in the air *over* the continent than

163]

there was water in the rivers flowing *off* the continent. This fact intrigued him.

The other man kept his attention fixed on the ground. Suddenly he exclaimed, "Look what I see!" He stooped over and picked up a gold object. It was not a nugget; it was an old gold watch. The front and back were protected by covers. The stem released the front cover, and there, underneath a heavy glass crystal, were the hands of a watch that moved over a Roman numeral face. There were VIII divisions on the dial instead of the usual XII. None of the other markings on the watch could be understood. The two men began to speculate about the watch. What kind of time did the watch keep? To whom did it belong? Who made it?

One of the men was able to believe only what he could see and read. He postulated that since no owner or maker could be established for the watch, it must have come to be there by chance and that chance processes in nature had brought about this object. The other man postulated that behind the watch there must have been some very intelligent personality and that this person must have possessed many skills to produce such an intricate mechanism. He even went so far as to say that he would have liked to get acquainted with the maker of the watch, if he could have been found.

Much like these men are meteorologists when they see rain falling on a field. The rain to them represents one of the principal ingredients of the science they follow—water vapor. Water vapor is a member of the trinity of meteorology: pressure, temperature, and humidity. Although no meteorological process takes place without these three, water vapor is the dominant factor. Even though water is a common substance, it is only just now being discovered. It presents many puzzling problems which are only partially understood.

Measurement of Water Vapor Density

Of the three elements mentioned, water vapor density, or humidity, is the hardest to measure. One of the reasons that meteorologists cannot forecast the weather better, let alone control the rainfall or prevent violent storms, is that they cannot measure water vapor as precisely as they would like to measure it.

Humidity measurements are not so difficult at temperatures above freezing and in ordinary amounts, but when the temperature goes below freezing the problem becomes more complicated. If we use the conventional wet- and dry-bulb thermometers, the difference between the wet- and dry-bulb temperatures is upset. The dry bulb measures the dry air temperature, but the wet bulb, instead of indicating the wet-bulb temperature, measures the freezing point of water. The readings are meaningless until all the water is turned to ice in the film over the wet bulb; then the wet-bulb temperature indicates the true equilibrium temperature. It takes considerable time to establish this balance at subfreezing temperatures. This difficulty greatly hinders the usefulness of the wet- and dry-bulb psychrometer for the measurement of moisture below freezing on an aircraft (often used in weather studies).

In all hygrometers (general name for instruments measuring the degree of moisture in the atmosphere) which depend on the deposit of a film of water or ice on a surface to indicate humidity, the water vapor has another property which produces confusion. Water can exist in either of two states at temperatures below freezing: as a supercooled liquid or as ice. The water vapor density over supercooled water is different from that over ice, for the same temperature. The result is that one is not sure which state of the vapor he is measuring. This difficulty, however, is not so serious as the wet-bulb problem just mentioned.

The problem of the measurement of water vapor density at temperatures below freezing is presently being solved by the use of a new type of instrument—the optical absorption hygrometer, or humidiometer. This instrument uses invisible ultraviolet light. The radiation is transmitted through the lithium fluoride window of a hydrogen lamp across a measuring path and through the lithium fluoride window of a nitric oxide ion chamber (ions are electrified particles), where it produces an electric current. This current is a function (indicates the state) of the water vapor density in the measuring path. This radiation at a wavelength of 1,216 angstroms is very sensitive to the presence of water vapor. With this method water vapor densities corresponding to dew-point temperatures (temperatures at which vapor begins to change to liquid) from $+15°$ to $-15°$ C. have been measured. Changes of moisture which take place in one-hundredth of a second can be detected with this airborne psychrometer.

The reason for the improvement in airborne vapor measurement is that invisible light is used. This is like trying to find out about God. God is invisible, although many of the manifestations of His presence are visible. If one depends only on his senses to learn about God, he is greatly limited. In anyone's learning about God faith is the invisible light of the spiritual realm. According to the Bible, "faith is the substance of things hoped for, the evidence of things not seen." (Heb. 11:1, AV)

The Omnipresence of Water Vapor

Water vapor is an omnipresent substance. While small amounts of water vapor may be hard to detect, water vapor is something that cannot possibly be eliminated. To obtain absolutely dry air is practically impossible. Trying to obtain such dry air is like the classic problem of the dog that chased a rabbit. Each minute the dog decreased the distance between himself and the rabbit by one-half. When did the dog catch the rabbit? The answer is never. So it is with water vapor. Suppose one has a chamber, and each minute he evacuates one-half the amount of water vapor in the chamber. When does the chamber become dry? The answer is never. So far, the driest substance to use as a zero reference for the humidiometer is dry nitrogen gas.

The omnipresence of water is like that of God. The psalmist said, "Whither shall I go from thy spirit? or whither shall I flee from thy presence? If I ascend up into heaven, thou art there: if I make my bed in hell, behold, thou art there. If I take the wings of the morning, and dwell in the uttermost parts of the sea; even there shall thy hand lead me, and thy right hand shall hold me. If I say, Surely the darkness shall cover me; even the night shall be light about me." (Ps. 139: 7-11, AV) Sometimes man seems to be in a fog when he searches for God. His vision is very limited. But even in nature layers of fog may be channels of unlimited vision.

Anomalous Radio Propagation at Very High and Ultrahigh Frequency

Airborne measurements of water vapor with fast response instruments have enabled us to measure dry and moist layers in the atmosphere. These measurements have told us that anomalous (abnormal) propagation conditions at v.h.f. and u.h.f. are produced at the interface between dry and moist layers in the atmosphere. This interface acts as an open-air wave guide, which channels the high-frequency energy to distances many miles beyond the horizon. This energy usually can be detected only over a line-of-sight distance of about thirty nautical miles because of the curvature of the earth. By flying in this dry-moist air interface, an airborne receiver can detect signals thousands of miles beyond the horizon of the transmitting station.

Measurements of these layers have been made in many places. Some of these measurements were made between the coast of Brazil and Ascension Island in the South Atlantic, a distance of more than 1,000 nautical miles; between the California coast and Hawaii, a distance of more than 2,000 nautical miles; and over the Pacific Ocean between Honolulu and Canton Island. The phenomenon has also been observed over the Indian Ocean, the Arabian Sea, the Mediterranean Sea, and the Atlantic Ocean.

Usually these layers are visible to the naked eye and can be seen as stratus clouds or haze layers. When these layers are in subsiding air over a relatively cold water surface, very steep water vapor gradients (slopes) are established at the temperature inversion produced by the subsiding air. When an aircraft flies in this layer, the visibility is reduced sometimes to less than 1,000 feet. The pilot has to have special permission to fly in such clouds. Signals can be detected far beyond the horizon if the aircraft has a v.h.f. or u.h.f. radio or radar set on board.

When an aircraft flies in a fog without some other form of vision, it is in danger. So it is with people. We need to see beyond our horizons. The Book of Proverbs says, "Where there is no vision, the people perish. . . ." (Ch. 29:18, AV) Not only is it desirable to have extended vision, but without it we are also in danger. We can obtain this vision through the Bible.

The Wavelike Structure of a Very Thin Water Vapor Layer

A very interesting observation of wavelike structure occurred in a flight over Chesapeake Bay. Two humidiometer sensors were spaced 6 feet apart, one above the other, in undisturbed air, and a vertical sounding was made. The output of each humidiometer sensor was presented on a two-channel oscilloscope (instrument for showing changes in a current) so that the fluctuations of each sensor could be compared. The normal fluctuation was for both outputs to be in unison, but at 8,250 feet above the bay, as the aircraft was descending slowly, it was observed that the fluctuations of the two sensors were out of phase. This seemed strange and presented a problem, which had to be explained. The pilot was told to climb, and soon the sensors were fluctuating in unison again. A slow descent was then made through the layer, and the same phenomenon was observed again. When the thin layer, less than 6 feet in depth, had been penetrated, the sensors began to fluctuate in unison again. This peculiar behavior seemed to indicate that the sensors, which were spaced 6 feet apart, were so positioned that one of them was above a filament layer of water vapor, and the other below the layer. In other words, we had been flying with the layer *between* the two 6-feet-apart sensors.

When the data for the flight were analyzed, it was found that the minimum change in water vapor produced a tiny variation of water vapor pressure (0.2 millibars). At the temperature of the environment this amount of moisture change caused a difference of 0.9 N units (N units are units of dry nitrogen gas, a substance used as a zero reference for the humidiometer, the water vapor measuring machine) in a distance of 6 feet, or a gradient of 150 N units per 1,000 feet. A gradient of 49 N units per 1,000 feet is sufficient to give a radio beam a curvature equal to that of the earth, or to produce anomalous radio propagation. The length of the waves in the thin layer was about 20 feet.

There are still many things to learn about the distribution of water vapor in the air. One of these problems is the identification of "angels." "Angels" are seen frequently on a radar screen but cannot be detected with the naked eye. It has been suggested that they are swarms of insects, birds, or parcels of water vapor. So far this problem and many others have not been solved. Many times in physical research we do not get all the answers or even partial answers because of our limited comprehension. At other times we do not apply ourselves sufficiently. Learning about God, too, is in many ways a progressive revelation, just like studying the problems of science, which are oftentimes revealed to us in proportion to the intelligent application we make.

Hexagonal Shapes in Thin Fluid Layers and Snowflakes

The study of thin layers of liquid or gas has shown that hexagonal (six-sided) circulation cells can be set up in the layer when there is a strong temperature gradient (slope) across the layer. This can be done by pouring ether into a dish. The rapid evaporation from the surface of the liquid cools the top, but the bottom of the layer is heated by the plate. Hexagonal circulation cells are thus established. The same type of circulation may be established in thin layers of smoke, water vapor, or water when the layer is heated from below. Of course, because of the shape of the vessel or other factors, all the cells may not be hexagonal in shape, but the preferred cell structure is hexagonal.

There may be no relationship between the hexagonal cell structure of thin fluid layers and snowflake formation. The processes are not completely understood. There are unsolved problems here. But the preferred structure of snowflakes is also hexagonal. No two snowflakes are exactly alike, but still the preferred shape of the flake is six-sided. This phenomenon belongs to the mysteries of water.

Even though these problems are not understood, there is a suggestion of order and of a designer in the processes. If one tossed a die 600 times, the laws of chance would dictate that in the total casts each of the 6 faces would come up about 100 times. But if the 6 face came up 600 times, one would be justified in saying that the die had been designed to operate that way. If he were gambling with such a die, his opponents would say that it was dishonest and that the game had been rigged. What does this tell us about God? It becomes increasingly evident that there is a Designer behind the processes described.

Air Cells in the Trade Winds

The hexagonal shape of large-scale convective (upward or downward moving) air cells in the trade winds is not observable, although it may be present. In the trade wind moisture layer the air between the sea surface and the trade wind temperature inversion (to warmer air) is heated from below. Convective (rising or falling) circulations are set up. These cells may have diameters of ten to thirty miles. If there is a wind shear at the top of the layer, the cumulus clouds marking the rising currents of air in the cell become spread out and make cloud streets—*i.e.*, there is a band of cloud, then a band of clear sky, alternately. This type of cloud

[170

formation is commonly seen from aircraft flying over the trade wind belt.

Not only has this phenomenon been observed from aircraft, but now that weather satellites are observing clouds from above, a much broader overall picture can also be seen of the large-scale cloud formations. Satellite pictures reveal that some of the cells have a rising core, marked by cumulus cloud growth, and other cells have sinking cores, indicated by clear spots at the center of the cell. It is not understood why some cells should have ascending currents of air, and others descending currents, or what the critical factor is that determines whether the cell core should be a rising or a sinking current. This information is, of course, important, but the problem still awaits solution.

In this connection one is reminded of the words of Jesus to Nicodemus: "The wind bloweth where it listeth, and thou hearest the sound thereof, but canst not tell whence it cometh, and whither it goeth. . . ." (John 3:8, AV) Jesus compared this phenomenon of nature with spiritual things. One accepts the facts of nature without understanding them, so why should one despair when he cannot understand all the spiritual things?

Water Vapor Provides a Check on Temperature Extremes

One of the meteorological phenomena which are widely accepted but not completely understood is the air mass thunderstorm. Not all of the convective (rising and falling) air cells are confined within the temperature inversion (warmer temperature), as in the case of the trade wind cells, but some of them penetrate it from the outside. What happens then? With increased heating and the accompanying rise in temperature at the surface, the air parcels rise and begin to cool until they reach the condensation level—*i.e.*, the place where moisture condenses and becomes visible as a cloud. After the condensation level has been reached, the rate of cooling of the air parcels increases greatly. This latter lapse (decrease of temperature) is irreversible, whereas the precondensation stage is reversible.

Suppose now that there is no temperature inversion (warmer temperature), as in the case of the trade wind cells, to oppose the rising current of air and that the temperature of the surrounding air mass is also such that it cannot restrain the rising current; then, in such a case, this parcel of rising air keeps ascending by its own buoyancy until it is forcibly checked by a temperature inversion at a very high altitude—30,000 to 40,000 feet.

This is what happens in a thunderstorm, according to the parcel theory, which is not correct in *all* respects. In the ascending parcel, moisture is being condensed, and part of it falls out as rain or hail. Some of it evaporates and goes back to the vapor state again. Of course, all this does not happen as quietly and gradually as it has been described here. Sometimes these updrafts assume tremendous proportions. Updrafts in severe thunderstorms of 5,000 feet per minute have been reported, followed by downdrafts of 2,000 feet per minute.

What is the result of this condensation, evaporation, and violent mixing? One of the results is that the rise of the afternoon temperature is checked by cool rain and cool air. Not only does water vapor prevent the rise of extreme temperatures in the afternoon, but it also checks the fall of temperature on a clear cold night. If one should measure the temperature and dew point (the point at which vapor begins to change to liquid) in the evening—say, after the thunderstorm—he would be surprised to see that the minimum temperature the next morning would not be less than the evening dew point. If the sky were covered all night by low clouds (less than 10,000 feet) or if there were strong winds aloft, the temperature would probably be higher than the evening dew point. This is because the ground radiates heat through a clear sky more rapidly than through a cloudy sky or through turbulent air. When the ground radiates heat (infrared radiation), the temperature at the surface falls, but this fall is checked by the latent (unnoticed) heat of condensation of water vapor when dew or frost is formed. This supply of heat is sufficient to prevent the temperature from falling below the dew point. During the spring, many fruit and vegetable crops have been saved from frost damage by water vapor. Water vapor brings comfort by checking both high and low temperatures.

Water Sustains All Life

In our physical world water vapor not only protects life from temperature extremes, but is also essential to life. Without moisture in our atmosphere suffocating dust clouds would roll over the earth. Water is as essential to life as air. Plants, fish, animals, and man—all need water to sustain life. *How* water sustains life is a mystery, perhaps as mysterious as life itself. It is one of our greatest unsolved problems. Yet we accept water and thankfully use it, our limited knowledge of it notwithstanding.

Like the gold watch found in the field after the rain shower, water challenges our curiosity. We too would like to know more about it, especially about who made it. We would even like to get acquainted with its Maker.

As for its Maker, the Bible expresses it this way: "All things were made by him (Christ); and without him was not any thing made that was made." (John 1:3, AV) That is certainly putting it in a clear and most emphatic way. And the same Christ thought and spoke often of that wonderful substance He had made and one time used it for one of His great illustrations—a bit of truly Oriental imagery: "Whosoever drinketh of this water shall thirst again: but whosoever drinketh of the water that I shall give him shall never thirst; but the water that I shall give him shall be in him a well of water springing up into everlasting life." (John 4:13,14, AV) Some meteorologists think fondly of this when they see rain coming down on a parched field, or study the cloud formations, or measure water vapor density.

GROPING ABOUT IN
THE SPACE AGE

BY MERLIN WAYNE ZOOK

METEOROLOGIST

The writer of this chapter is one of our younger scientists and a specialist in air pollution for the State of Pennsylvania. He has a degree from Goshen College, where his specialty was physical science, and was graduated with a Ph.D. from Pennsylvania State University, where he majored in synoptic meteorology. He has other diversified scientific interests: applied mathematics, astronomy, geology, and hydrology. Readers will no doubt be interested in the frank opinions and lucid statements of an avant-garde, up-and-coming American scientist.

RATHER loftily, we call this the space age. But we know very little about space, even about the extremely small space that the earth and we earthmen occupy.

Meteorology has much to do with the space immediately surrounding the earth. It deals with the atmosphere and its phenomena—heat, cold, rain, and wind. As a science, it is still young, far younger than, for instance, astronomy, which seems to have been cradled in ancient Egypt. In fact, meteorology did not reach any sizable stature until the Second World War, a rather recent date.

At present this science is making significant headway with developments in objective weather forecasting, especially by the use of computers. The science consists of a complex pattern of mathematics, physics, and chemistry, and for that reason presents a veritable multitude of unsolved problems, a limited number of which will be touched on in this chapter. In doing so, we are bound to think of Job's words to Bildad: ". . . the thunder of his (God's) power who can understand?" (Job 26:14, AV)

Our Creator caused the earth to have an electric field. Both the surface and the atmosphere of the earth act like a charged plate in a battery—the surface being negatively, the atmosphere positively, charged. Measurements have disclosed that a man 6 feet tall has a potential of about 260 volts from the soles of his feet to the top of his head. He does not feel electric shock since the flow of electricity is slow. This electric potential is similar over the entire surface of the earth, although it decreases with altitude. Strange to say, the field has a daily variation. Meteorologist O. H. Gish says that in London, England, a minimum of variation occurs about three o'clock in the morning, and a maximum at six o'clock in the evening.

In stormy weather the electric field is disturbed with sudden voltage increases, ranging to ten and more times the normal value of the undisturbed field. A theory set forth to explain this maintenance of the earth's electric field states that numerous thunderstorms over the earth's surface maintain the charge. Quantitative investigations, however, of the violent electric fields in these storms are insufficient and inconclusive. Actually the mechanism of the maintenance of the earth's electric field remains unexplained. The great problem is still a problem indeed.

The intricate mechanisms in clouds that cause rain, snow, and other types of precipitation are also not understood by our meteorologists. The exact process that causes water vapor to be transformed into droplets is unknown. To make this problem more complex, the mysteries of condensation, cloud nuclei, and drop-size distribution have never really been fathomed. These processes present several closely related problems which yield a larger complex problem. The Creator certainly provided man with a deep and dark, so far inscrutable mystery in such ostensibly simple things as rain and snow.

Meteorologists believe that rain begins in the form of snow. How, then, do the small snow crystals originate? A process, called sublimation (elevation or exaltation), in which vapor is transformed directly into ice crystals without passing through the liquid stage is credited with the crystal formation. But in the complex atmosphere, where cooled and supercooled droplets exist, the sublimation process remains a mystery. In fact, does it really exist? The growth of rain droplets and their resultant sizes are functions of collision and coalescence, but to what magnitude each of these operates is not clear. One theory stated that rain could fall only from clouds in which both ice crystals and raindrops were present. But rain fell from all-water clouds in the tropical regions, so the scientists were once more confused.

Since these phenomena are difficult to discern, is it any wonder that the forecasting of precipitation is a tough assignment for meteorologists? Then there are several factors—such as when and where precipitation will occur, the amounts of precipitation, and the relationship of precipitation patterns to the winds aloft—meteorologists must consider in their forecasting. A lack of knowledge of the intricate mechanisms already mentioned, together with these other weather factors, makes precipitation forecasting a difficult procedure. But the unsolved problem of how rain originates is the basic difficulty. Whether it will please our Creator-God to allow scientific man, sooner or later, to raise the curtain on this or that mystery or eventually on all the mysteries in the field of meteorology is, of course, a question no mere man can answer. But the curtain is there, and it is heavy and definitely nontransparent. And the difference between Divine omniscience and present-day human limitations should be overabundantly clear.

"All things were made by him"—that is, by Christ. (John

1:3, AV) That includes the atmosphere. When the atmosphere was made, the atmosphere's motion, what we now call general circulation, was made. It is the general circulation's mechanism that causes the winds to blow and the weather to change. How is this general circulation maintained? What causes its different velocities? How far will a center of bad weather travel in one day? Why do the winds blow at high velocities aloft, in the upper regions?

Much of this we don't know. We do know that the regions of heat sources in the tropics and those of icy cold around the poles have a great deal to do with overall circulation, but to what extent or magnitudes and in what trajectories we cannot say. Nor can we say how the different ambient readings of temperature, humidity, vertical and horizontal winds, and air mass movements affect the circulation.

In the circulation are areas of low atmospheric pressure called cyclones. The laws of thermodynamics (heat power) and hydrodynamics (water power), which are relatively difficult to apply in pure physics, are near to impossible to apply in the study of cyclone systems. The sources of energy that keep the cyclones moving and developing are unknown. Indications point to such factors as the close juxtaposition of air masses that vary in temperature, density, and moisture, and the underlying land or water surfaces. But the magnitudes which each of these factors contributes toward a cyclone's violence or life-span are not known.

The counterpart of a cyclone is an area of high atmospheric pressure, or fair weather, called an anticyclone. There are cold highs and warm highs, and the one can be transformed into the other, leaving the meteorologists confused by the way this is accomplished. High-pressure cells may link or couple with cells aloft; this is another mystery. Like cyclones, anticyclones can grow and intensify, but the mechanisms are not known. The dynamic origin of an anticyclone, as well as that of a cyclone, remains unsolved. The fact that the winds blow westward near the equator and eastward elsewhere, reversing at times until the poles are reached, is another conundrum. We are sure there are clear and definite solutions to all these problems and a great many others of a more technical nature, but so far the solutions lie hidden in the Lord's own inscrutable, all-comprehending mind.

Meteorologists also have given a great deal of thought to the sun, the enormous flaming ball of fire which at a distance of some 90,000,000 miles is, of course, bound to affect our weather. But exactly *how* does it affect the weather? In which bands of its spectrum does it influence the weather to the largest degree? Do the infrared or the ultraviolet rays play a significant part? Or does only the visible part of the spectrum have a dominant role? Do sunspots, those immense storms on the sun's surface, cause weather anomalies, a trend toward colder or warmer temperatures over a long period of time in different regions? The sun emits fast-moving atomic particles, which constantly bombard the upper air. If these particles affect the upper air, how is the change transported downward to the regions of the active weather? Long-range weather forecasting might develop if the sun's influence on the atmosphere were better known. But it isn't. Again we face an array of divers problems.

Then there are the violent windstorms and thunderstorms. For a thousand and one practical reasons people would like to know when and where these severe weather manifestations will occur. Associated with these storms, on rather frequent occasions, are tornadoes, violent whirls of wind with a funnel-shaped cloud. These funnels strike unexpectedly in places where they are least anticipated. How to forecast a touchdown of a funnel is entirely unknown. So little is known about the internal structure of thunderstorms and tornadoes because the violence of these weather phenomena prevents us from probing into their mysteries.

There are laws of thermodynamics and hydrodynamics operating on the earth. These laws are gradually being applied to general weather forecasting on a large scale. Computers are being used in the Northern Hemisphere to solve complicated equations. These computers turn out sheets of

[178

paper with numerals arranged on them in unique patterns, which in turn are decoded and replotted on the weather map. This map is the forecast map for the next six or twenty-four hours—no more. Accuracy has been fair. But to use these maps as local weather forecasts, for counties or even for states, is hardly warranted, and improvement in computer service is needed. Other problems arise in computer forecasting: The development and intensification of cyclones or anticyclones are not accounted for in the dynamic equations (power estimates); the change of wind direction with height is not predicted correctly; turbulence is not considered; the eastward movement of storms is overaccelerated; and stationary storm centers (places of lowest pressure) are being displaced westward. The computer can use only the values which man gives to it, and man certainly does not know all the answers! The computer has not yet outperformed God's mind or guessed His various intentions.

This writer likes to dwell in his mind on the stratosphere, a region of stable air above the turbulent troposphere and a place of many outstanding phenomena. It is a strange region, in a way, and a region of supernal beauty—beauty the way God conceives and paints it. There are the noctilucent clouds. Noctilucent means "light at night." The clouds were given this name because the sun shines on them long after dark. They are in the lighted portion of the atmosphere when it is dark on the earth's surface. They are gold and red and brown near the horizon, and blue and white at higher altitudes. The explanation? We do not know, because the usual reasons for lower region color schemes among the clouds do not apply. There are mother-of-pearl clouds, too, in the stratosphere, looking like real mother-of-pearl, with blue, green, red, and lilac colors, just in this order, running from the edges of the clouds to their centers. This phenomenon also has never been explained satisfactorily. True, the phenomena have been attributed to water vapor or waves in the warm, dry, and stable stratosphere, but man's penetrations into this layer of the atmosphere have been so rare and studies and

179]

investigations have been so random and intermittent that the real mechanism of these and other unusual phenomena remains scientifically unknown. Then, of course, there is always the possibility that the phenomena, even after thorough study, might *remain* unexplainable to mortal and imperfect man, even to the end of earthly time. "For we know in part . . ." (I Cor. 13:9, AV)—also in things material and terrestrial.

In writing these paragraphs, I have but scratched the surface of meteorological problems. Most of such problems are highly technical. But, technical or nontechnical, they all speak of a mind that far excels any human mind or combination of human minds. They speak with clarion voice of a Mind Divine. They speak of the old Bible concepts of omniscience, omnipotence, and an unflagging, ever-continuing sustenance by God of His entire creation.

NUCLEAR KNOWLEDGE TEACHES
DEEP HUMILITY

BY JOHN J. GREBE

NUCLEAR SCIENTIST, RESEARCHER

IN ELECTROCHEMISTRY, ETC.

Without doubt Dr. Grebe is one of the world's greatest scientists, although as a humble man he might not approve our saying so. Starting out as something of a prodigy, he made his way through Cleveland's Technical High School with honors and then captured Case Institute of Technology's B.Sc., M.Sc., and D.Sc. degrees in easy succession. He has been a member of the Dow Chemical Company since 1924 and holds more than sixty patents in electrochemistry, synthesis of organic compounds, nuclear reactors, and the like. He did extensive research in electrometric analysis, electrolysis of fused salts, high-temperature cracking processes for making butadiene and synthetic rubber, plus theoretical work on gravity and time cycles. Dr. Grebe for a long time was the director of Dow's Nuclear and Basic Research Department. He was a member of the Advisory Committee of Radiation and Isotope Development for the U.S. Atomic Energy Commission, a civilian observer at the Bikini tests, and the chief scientific adviser to the chief of the Army Chemical Corps, and he filled many other highly responsible positions. The scientific organizations that count Dr. Grebe among their honored members are too numerous to mention here.

SOME people find God by studying the vast cosmos, recognizing that all of man's doings do not even represent a grain of sand among all the grains of sand on all the beaches of all the oceans of the earth. They observe distances, velocities, masses, and densities of matter that stagger them.

Others find God by sharing a strange depth of feeling, by a singular beauty of the soul, and by the self-sacrificing devotion of the many noble people whom one finds in all walks of life. A loving and understanding glance of the eye still makes man's technical achievements trivial, compared with the soul with which we were endowed. Still others meet God among the suffering and severely tried people who recognize that our life on earth is a training ground for faith.

Strange to say, perhaps, but there are also people who are led to thoughts of God by industrial development. Engineering and applied sciences in production industry, in transportation, and in communications impress one. So do the marvels of jet travel, with personal television reception and tasty food made possible by modern methods that imitate natural processes with very crude but powerful machinery. Very impressive, also, are the great power and usefulness that are being wrested by man from the energy reservoirs of the atoms.

But this impressiveness and consequent deep humility in sensitive men are hardly to be compared with those which are occasioned by the new molecular biology and, beyond this, by the submolecular properties of living matter. It is now recognized that the very tune sung by each electron whirling around the nucleus of its hydrogen atom when the atom is living differs by precisely measured rates from the same structure of the atom when it is dead. This is measured by new instruments, which grip the molecule in a magnetic vise and then twang it as though it were a reed, to amplify its natural oscillations. It is called electron spin resonance.

Similarly, the nucleus itself also responds to many variations in its continuous song, trying its best to keep in harmony with the millions of atoms joined with it in the molecule. This is measured as nuclear magnetic moment.

The new knowledge being accumulated at a very rapid

[182

rate is differentiating finer details than were recognized before. It is even possible to tell whether any one of the 64 subgroups in any one DNA molecule, called amino acid groups, is placed right side up in the steps of the beautiful spiral-stairway-shaped key to differentiating one species from another. All the old notions of tracing man's relations to other forms of life by shape or by comparisons of embryos are now thoroughly discredited by the fact that while some mammals have only 2 DNA groups (out of 64) that differ, man's DNA code differs in 17 of the groups. What is more, nuclear properties are now showing more distinctions (between man and other forms of life) than the microscope added to ordinary visual observations 100 years ago.

No wonder some old-time biologists disdainfully refer to the new molecular science as the holy trinity—even in public print. How can an instrument that comes out with jiggles in a line have meaning to them, compared with instruments or tools used in vivisections? How can a mere molecule, a tiny speck, have the capacity to convey information to transfer traits of personality, quirks of mannerisms, and fantastic likeness in voice and features?

But oh, how many details can be presented in even one atom! The nucleus is only about one hundred-millionth as big in diameter as the atom itself. So when one knows that the unit of length that can determine detail (like the dimensions of the bricks used to build a city) is so exceedingly fine when compared with the whole, the reservoir of information in a large molecule is truly great.

It is well recognized that the human brain has a memory capacity that is immense, compared with the marvelous brains that store and transmit pictures and information in our satellites. It would take three Empire State Buildings chock-full of such satellite "brains" to equal one human brain. No wonder, then, that the DNA code molecule, with its associated RNA and its enzymes, can contain the information required to procreate any one species. What is more, all the various species—whether an ameba, a plant, or man—

183]

have the same molecular complexity, with sixty-four amino group components to their DNA. Each species is represented by a sixty-four-letter code word from an alphabet of twenty letters. There is no chance of one being built on the other by compounding, just as the words of our language have evolved. Any damage in the DNA code molecule, even the turning around of one component in its proper place, has been found to be lethal (deadly) and prevents reproduction. So there can be no fortuitous accidents that transpose one kind to another. All the millions of efforts with X rays for mutations of fruit flies or plants, using large colonies and assortments of them, have produced no new kinds whatsoever. A current report on the hereditary effects of the intense exposure to atom bombs in Japan informs us that any kind of measurable effect is absent, whereas the resulting degeneration from the marriage of first cousins in the same population is detectable.

If all this does not put man's notions in place, let us think beyond the currently measurable differences in molecules and atoms. A nuclear resonance phenomenon—the Mossbauer effect—now measures displacements of 1 part in 10,000,000,000. It is sensitive enough to prove that matter gains weight with velocity, as predicted by Einstein. Even this is coarse, compared with what we know is to be measured in the future. It is Max Planck's "length," as basic to all physical science as Planck's "constant," a measure of action.

Now, this length is only one part in a hundred billion-billionth of the smallest dimension the very powerful atom smashers are capable of detecting about the diameter of the nucleus. Today it is as though we had circumnavigated the nucleus—as though it were a continent, like Australia, and we had seen its shores, mountains, and rivers around the periphery and knew that there were an immense area and depth to be explored for all kinds of living organisms, minerals, and maybe oil. And we must go exploring. It is this kind of exploring that is planned with the new billion-dollar accelerator that is being designed at the present time. If very successful, it will tell us about structure only ten times as fine as that already known. The rest of our exploratory efforts may have to be left to our children. They can possibly handle the other multiple billions—if there is time left!

Even now it is possible to hypothesize that the length is the interval between crisscrossing paths of charges in motion, at the velocity of light, within the components of the nucleus. It is these dimensions that can be used to explain gravity as the residual electrostatic attraction between spinning electrons and positrons of nuclei acting on distant masses of nuclei.

Only the broad perspective of the trivial fraction of human knowledge, compared with what is still to be known, can enable man to get some impression of the astounding beauty, order, and detail in life and the universe that some people actually say just happened by chance. As for unsolved problems, the seeming unsolvableness of many of them and the multiplicity of all of them are implied in the material discussed so far. Man has made important advances on the road of knowledge, and we rejoice in it; but there is no denying that he has encountered, and still encounters, any number of pitfalls and roadblocks. Any real scientist is a struggler—but a struggler going onward and upward and with a quickening song of valor in his heart.

Any real scientist is also humble, just because he has to struggle and especially because he is deeply cognizant of his limitations and the boundless greatness of the Master Craftsman. The greater the man, the more humble he is before his Creator. Einstein's God was ever so much greater than the God we generally preach and teach. Most of us everyday scientists do not study the various sciences from a truly *scientific* point of view. We have our personal ideas; we have been influenced by big names; we have succumbed to a certain kind of listless, stagnating mental atmosphere. Einstein, by whom so many swear, was a believer in God, and when he was asked about a chance or haphazard origin of life and the universe, he squelched the notion by simply saying, "God does not throw dice."

Some of our religious leaders, too, should be cautioned not to parrot without exhaustive investigation the many theories about the origin of things paraded by men who labor in science and are outspoken disbelievers in God. It is not only spurious theories about cosmogony (origination of the world) but also unrestrained speculations about the chronology of the earth and celestial bodies that have made a strong appeal to certain spiritual guides who should know better. Most of those speculations have shaky foundations; others are entirely baseless.

There is, for a lone example, the carbon 14 question. Recent thinking, guided by carbon 14 dating, would have us believe that the Bible is entirely mistaken in its intimations of the age of the earth. We were asked to think of at least 100,000 years when trying to calculate the earth's age, and many men proposed figures many times that size. Those who refused to accept any such gigantic figures were judged back numbers.

According to some of the very latest scientific reports, carbon 14 dating is not very dependable. In fact, our geologists may have to change some of their thinking very rapidly. The recent pictures of the moon and of Mars have contributed their share to this proposed modification, but earnest independent study did most of it.

In my judgment, these authors of some of the latest scientific reports are making a sensible move. We know that water is continually being generated in outer space within the earth's magnetic field by the reaction between sloweddown solar protons forming hydrogen and water crystals with oxygen. We also know from very recent correlations that the earth's magnetic field appears to have reversed a number of times. One such reversal could well have been the cause of Noah's Deluge. At such a time the portion of the waters that were above the firmament could have come down, being swept by cosmic rays and solar winds, when the magnetic

[186

field, heretofore acting as a shield, was passing through zero strength. The mile or so of water added by the Deluge would have shielded the earth before this. Even the nitrogen in the air would have been shielded from the neutrons that now produce carbon 14.

So, suddenly, geologists may discover that the elaborate carbon 14 dating of up to 100,000 years or more has collapsed to a relatively short time after the great Flood. All the long periods based on old thinking would have to be redated. All the isotope dating based on uranium, helium and many other elements would then become the logical result of a moon- and Mars-like phase of the earth when it was "without form and void; and darkness was upon the face of the deep" (Gen. 1:2, AV) and before God provided light and its radiant energy.

The collection of the meteors and dust at the time of the Deluge collapsed by the increased force of gravity and the thousands of pounds per square inch of added weight. This in turn generated heat that melted most of the earth's core, producing immense volcanic action and releasing the combined waters. Heavy isotope dating would thus become as irregular and meaningless as the variations in samples seem to indicate and as it would be on Mars.

How wonderful it would be if further data from space and the orientation of magnetite crystals in viscous lava flows would continue to clarify the details of the biblical creation and flood accounts! The vertical components of the magnetization data should be most revealing.

THE ENDURING MYSTERY
OF MATTER

BY WILLIAM G. POLLARD

PHYSICIST—SPECIALIST

IN ATOMIC STRUCTURE

AND FUNCTION

Dr. Pollard is the distinguished founder and the executive director of the Oak Ridge Institute of Nuclear Studies, in Oak Ridge, Tennessee. The institute is famous the world over; is sponsored by no fewer than thirty-eight universities; operates in direct contact with the U.S. Atomic Energy Commission; carries on constant experimentation for the physical betterment of the human race; and engages in a great variety of practical endeavors of a humanitarian nature. Dr. Pollard, like the institute, is internationally known and respected. He was graduated from the University of Tennessee and, thereafter, from Rice Institute with a Ph.D., and he was a consulting physicist to large industrial corporations, a professor of physics at the University of Tennessee, and a research scientist at Columbia University and the SAM laboratories. In the course of his labors he was so affected by the wealth of scientific evidence indicating God's existence that he accepted the highly solemn fact for himself and then began to wonder if he shouldn't tell others about it. He prepared himself for the ministry and today continues as an active front-rank scientist and as the minister of St. Stephen's Episcopal church, in Oak Ridge, where large audiences of educated people listen to him. He is indefatigable in his labors at Oak Ridge and is the author of many notable scientific monographs. In the present chapter Dr. Pollard gives a clear description of atomics in the language of the common man—the first such description, so far as we know, ever undertaken by an expert.

MATTER, any physical matter, is a most marvelous product of the hand of God.

Matter presents itself to our immediate experience in a great diversity of forms. For primitive man there were first the major divisions between sea and earth and sky. Each of these domains contained its own diversity. The dry land had sand and soil, rocks and minerals, trees and grass. In the sky were air and rain, wind and storm, and above all the mysterious sun, moon, and stars. The sea was a vast immensity of water, in which the creatures that disported themselves were both small and great and which served as well for the nourishment of man's body as for the terror of his soul. Yet all of this, in one way or another, was matter.

Is there some secret hidden in the heart of matter which gives unity to this bewildering diversity? Can the imagination and the reason of man probe under the surface of his immediate experience and unmask this secret? It is a fascinating question, and from time to time in the long history of speculative thought it has been a dominant factor.

In the initial stage of Greek philosophy one possible clue was seized upon. Perhaps all could be understood in terms of four basic elements: air, fire, water, and earth. As a beginning, this scheme had much to commend it. After all, fire and earth were the ingredients from which iron, copper, and bronze were derived. Wind, water, and fire are commingled in storms. The combination of water and earth leads to fertility, and man, as was widely believed, was made of the dust of the earth but became a living being only when the breath of life was breathed into him. Here was certainly a first step in the long quest to unlock the inner secret of matter.

Later, in a more sophisticated vein, a genuine atomic theory of matter emerged with Leucippus and Democritus. One of the notions which led them to this theory was the thought of dividing any piece of matter into smaller and smaller halves. Ultimately, they agreed, one must come to a point where further division is impossible. Such a smallest or minimum piece of matter was an *atom* (from the Greek *atomos*, meaning uncut, indivisible). Later the philosopher Epicurus elaborated this line of thinking into a well-developed atomic theory of matter. As the common designation "epicurean" shows, he is best known today for his hedonism (the doctrine that pleasure is the chief end of life). This, however, resulted from the very recent date of the modern scientific atomic theory. Prior to it, the knowledge against which to evaluate the substantial achievement of Epicurus in this area of thought did not exist.

At the peak of the classical period a contemporary of Julius Caesar and Cicero, named Titus Lucretius Carus, wrote the most complete account of the atomic theory of matter which Greco-Roman philosophy produced. Lucretius was an extravagantly ardent admirer and follower of Epicurus. His sole work is a long epic poem on the nature of things, entitled *De Rerum Natura*. It is a unique contribution to the literature of mankind because, unlike other epics of similar length, it is not devoted to great human exploits and deeds but rather attempts to develop a complete and comprehensive scientific description of the whole universe. It covers the infinity of space, cosmology, the structure of matter; other worlds with their own earth, sun, and moon; the evolution of life and genetics; and the origin of man and his development from a primitive wild state to civilized societies. Nothing quite like it was attempted before or has been attempted since.

From our vantage point 2,000 years later, Lucretius shows many amazing flashes of insight. Yet in spite of these striking parallels to a modern scientific view of the nature of things, his entire poem is pure speculation based on general experience, untouched by the discipline of the slow and painstaking verification of ideas which has gradually built up our present view. Indeed, we gain an impression of his exceptional insight largely by selecting instances of his thoughts which agree with our view of things. There are, however, numerous instances in his poem of notions which are ludicrous from a modern vantage point. For example, he suggests that honey or syrup is made of smooth, round atoms, while bitter or acid foods are made of sharp-edged or barbed atoms.

Lucretius had little effect on his contemporaries, although Cicero admired his poem and was probably responsible for its preservation. But he was not widely read and had no discernible influence on subsequent thought. Indeed, the whole of Greek atomism had surprisingly little influence and seemed to be of little interest in the classical period. Only in the Renaissance was Lucretius rediscovered, and in the fifteenth and sixteenth centuries numerous editions of his poem were produced. It was only then that the idea of a systematic and unified view of nature, which was Lucretius' passionate vision, began to attract and excite the minds of men, both of those who admired Lucretius and of those who opposed him. He formed the link between the classical quest for the secret of matter and the new scientific quest, which began in the seventeenth century. To this quest and the strange depths of reality to which it has led us, we now turn.

The Chemical Atom of the Nineteenth Century

The idea of atoms as the elementary constituent of matter blossomed, as we have seen, in the Renaissance from the thin line it had followed through all the centuries from ancient Greece. At the dawn of modern science, at the beginning of the seventeenth century, it was popularized by the philosopher Gassendi and accepted by Galileo, Newton, and Boyle. But with all of them it remained a rather vague and general idea, unattached to any specific facts or processes. It was

191]

left to a Cumberland handloom weaver, named John Dalton, in the first decade of the nineteenth century to begin the process by which atoms became concrete and identifiable. This he did through the idea that atoms come in classes, with all atoms in each class being identical and each class constituting a chemical element. Although Lucretius thought of atoms running in classes, his classes were based on shape and geometrical form. The idea of chemical elements was distinctly new and, of course, turned out to be immensely fruitful.

As with all great ideas, this one had its preceding history, but we do not have the space to dilate on that. In time each chemical element was assigned a weight, its *atomic weight,* and careful experiments by Dalton and others showed that whenever two or more elements combined chemically to make a compound, the relative amounts had to be adjusted to fit a definite proportion if none of any of the elements was left over after the reaction was complete. Thus emerged the picture of all matter made up of a relatively small number of chemical elements, each one of which consisted of small, indivisible, and identical atoms. These elementary atoms combined in definite proportions to form molecules, which were the smallest units of compounds formed from two or more elements.

Throughout the nineteenth century this extremely fruitful idea was elaborated into a complete theory of the nature of matter, one far grander and more unified in scope and much more concrete in application than Lucretius had ever dreamed of. The Russian Mendeleev perfected the periodic arrangement of elements, which brought out the similarities of groups, such as chlorine, bromine, and iodine, and showed gaps pointing to as yet undiscovered elements. This arrangement also gave order to the idea of valence (the degree of combining power of an element), which pointed the way to systematizing the kinds of compounds which any given element could form.

In the second half of the century a great flowering of organic chemistry occurred, and the structures of a great variety of biologically important compounds were worked out. The vast variety of nature, both animate and inanimate, was surely and steadily yielding to the discovery of what seemed to be its innermost secret. That apparent secret was the underlying simplicity of some ninety elements whose atoms formed the irreducible and eternal constituents of all matter. With these atoms the well-nigh infinite variety of molecules could in principle, and increasingly in fact, be built in precise ways described by chemical formulas showing their exact structures. Not only could the nineteenth century confidently support Lucretius in saying that "sky, sea, lands, rivers, and sun, grains, trees, and breathing things" are put together out of these ninety elements, but it also could go further and show just how and precisely which combinations of the atoms were involved in each case.

Striking as this achievement was, the atomic theory of the nineteenth century went considerably beyond it by explaining a great variety of other phenomena with its atoms. The first step was the recognition that heat is mechanical energy at the atomic level. Many worthwhile experiments followed during the first half of the century. This line of development finally led to the formulation of thermodynamics as a completely general description of the behavior of heat in all physical or chemical systems. By the end of the century the properties of gases were well described in the kinetic theory (the theory of motion), and Maxwell and Boltzmann had developed statistical mechanics to a point at which it gave a detailed picture of the distribution of velocities among the molecules of a gas and the detailed manner in which atoms or molecules share energy among themselves and among the different ways in which they are free to move. The solid, liquid, and gaseous phases of matter were well understood in a general way.

It was an immense achievement of human understanding

—this atomic theory of the nineteenth century. When the century began, the idea of atoms had scarcely changed since Lucretius and his Greek atomist predecessors. As it came to a close, most of the elementary atoms of nature had been identified and their relative weights determined. A tremendous number of substances, metals, minerals, salts, fluids, gases, and numerous organic materials found in living systems had been precisely defined as specific combinations of these elements. The motions executed by these atoms or molecules had also been precisely defined. The several states in which matter is found were rather well understood in terms of forces between molecules and their motions. Much insight had been achieved in building an understanding of many of the mechanical and thermal (heat) properties of different substances in their solid or gaseous phases. The nature of matter was understood in a beautifully structured system of great internal consistency and elegance. Not only was this synthesis conceptually elegant, but it also authenticated itself by leading to many practical applications in synthetic chemicals, steam engines, internal-combustion engines, and the like.

In the first flush of enthusiasm over such an achievement in a bare 100 years of human history, the universal tendency was to think of nature as more or less transparent. The innermost secret of matter seemed to lie not far below the surface. The achievement was the result of many investigators' working in different fields on a variety of seemingly unrelated problems. Yet the results of their labors had often converged to bring out some new and unexpected aspect of the total picture. It was as though nature were a vast maze with many openings on its perimeter, through which scientists entered in search of its secrets. Yet as successive hurdles to understanding were overcome, the separate channels of the maze seemed to be leading to the one great secret at the center. Wherever one started at the surface, all would ultimately wind inward to this central principle at the heart of reality.

The Planetary Atom

The quest for the central secret of the nature of matter in the twentieth century has resulted in many surprises. Not the least of these is the realization that there still are great depths in the reservoir of nature's secrets. The feeling at the end of the nineteenth century that the explanation of matter lay just below the surface and that its major outlines had already been mapped out has proved to be quite deceptive. We have been plunged successively to three deeper levels below that reached at the beginning of the century. Each of these levels is something like a whole world, undergirding and explaining the one above it. Yet at each stage of exploration of one level the very existence of the level below was unrecognized until most of the exploration had been carried out.

Throughout this century the quest for the secret of matter has been an exciting one, filled with amazement and many surprises along the way. As a result, we no longer think of nature as shallow and of matter as basically simple and rather obvious when its secrets are revealed. On the contrary, nature seems to have inexhaustible depths, and matter is found to have inner structures and symmetries of great beauty which are neither simple nor obvious but rather intricate and strange.

The nineteenth-century atoms were hard elastic spheres, with no inner structure of their own and possessing mass as the sole basic property of the matter of which they were constituted. Yet parallel with the development of the atomic synthesis which the chemists and thermodynamicists were achieving, a number of physicists had been investigating an apparently unrelated phenomenon—electricity. When dissolved in water, a number of atoms showed the property of becoming electrically charged. Such charged atoms were called ions. Faraday had studied the process of electrolysis, familiar in electroplating and storage batteries. He had studied the process of ions in solution. The most important result of his investigations was to find that the amount of electricity on ions of all kinds was always a simple integral (necessary to completeness) multiple of a fundamental amount, either positive or negative, called in his honor the Faraday. More precisely, this was the minimum amount of electricity carried by a sufficient number of ions to make a mass in grams numerically equal to the atomic weight of their atoms. How many atoms were required to do this was not known at the time, so that the amount of mass and electric charge on each ion could not be determined.

In other studies it was found that metals and some other substances had the property of conducting electricity. A current of electric charge could be made to flow through them continuously under certain conditions. Different metals were characterized by offering different amounts of resistance to the flow of such a current. Yet for most of the century the relationship between these electrical properties of metals and of ions in solution and the developing atomic theory was not suspected. Electricity and magnetism were simply interesting auxiliary phenomena to be studied in their own right, but not apparently significant in the quest for the secret of matter and the atoms of which it is made.

Then, at the very end of the nineteenth century, Roentgen discovered X rays and J. J. Thomson discovered the electron. Suddenly, with these discoveries, electricity came to play a fundamental role in atomics. The new electrons were over 1,000 times less massive than even the lightest atom, yet they were clearly a constituent of matter. In the first quarter of the present century a series of brilliant experiments led to the development of the solar system model of atoms, which still remains the popular picture in the nonscientific world. Far from being pictured as the simple elementary spheres of the last century, atoms were now seen to be complex structures of more elementary particles. These particles are the neutron, proton, and electron. Each atom consists of a small central body, called the nucleus, which is made up of neutrons and protons and which contains almost all the mass of the atom. A number of negatively charged electrons, equal to the number of positively charged protons, then move around the central massive nucleus in planetlike orbits.

This picture of the nature of matter dramatically reduced the number of elements from the ninety-odd atoms of the chemists to just three basic elementary particles. Protons and neutrons could be combined in a variety of ways to obtain a rich assortment of nuclei. In these combinations the number of protons determined which of the chemical elements the nucleus would form when it collected its full complement of electrons. This is true because the chemical properties of the atom, such as the kinds of molecular compounds it would form and its position in the periodic table, depend only on the electrons circulating around the nucleus, not on the properties of the central nucleus itself. By analogy, we may suppose that if there are a number of other solar systems like ours, their differences from ours will depend on the number of planets in them, their size and mass, and the kinds of orbit they execute around their central suns. The stars at their centers would be very much like our sun.

In the case of atoms, those with one electron are hydrogen, those with six are carbon, those with twenty-six are iron, and those with ninety-two are uranium. Nuclei with the same number of protons, but different numbers of neutrons, are called isotopes of the same chemical elements. Thus, the simplest element, hydrogen, with only one proton and one electron, has three isotopes. The lightest and most common has no neutrons at all, and its nucleus consists of a single isolated proton. Heavy hydrogen, or deuterium, has a nucleus with one proton and one neutron, and a radioactive form of hydrogen called tritium has one proton and two neutrons in its nucleus.

With this picture of the atom, electricity came to be seen as an integral part of the structure of matter. Faraday's ions in solution, with their special properties in electrolysis, were seen to be atoms of their chemical element with one or more electrons removed from them or added to them. A metal

197]

such as copper could conduct electricity by having electrons move rather freely from atom to atom.

Perhaps the most striking result of this model of an atom was its application to the emission of light by atoms. Toward the end of the preceding century the brilliant work of Maxwell and Hertz had demonstrated that light is a wave motion of electric and magnetic fields and that these electromagnetic waves can be generated with suitable equipment so that radio and radar became possible. It was quickly seen that the characteristic light emitted by various atoms in a flame or an electric discharge, such as a neon tube, came from changes in the motions of the electrons in orbit in the individual atoms. In effect each atom could be regarded as a miniature radio or radar sending and receiving station. Thus, the phenomenon of light became intimately involved with atoms. Atoms as electric systems are the universal emitters and absorbers of light.

The Wave Atom

By the end of the first quarter of this century the solar system model of an atom as a heavy central nucleus with electrons swinging around it like planets around the sun had become firmly established. In the intervening forty years this model has been developed with great precision. Every aspect of atomic and molecular phenomena can be understood with great exactness and in minute detail. The central nucleus, consisting of neutrons and protons, has been explored in depth, and much of its structure and behavior is now understood. The way in which the outer electrons determine all the physical and chemical properties of different atoms is explained with clarity and accuracy. At this point in the unfolding of the twentieth century, science has achieved a truly comprehensive and satisfactory theoretical understanding of matter at its atomic and molecular level.

This comprehensive picture, however, has not been achieved without a very considerable sacrifice. This sacrifice

[198

has involved the abandonment of the simple conceptual model of the atom as a miniature planetary system, with electrons executing well-defined orbits. In its place a strange and somewhat intangible picture has been introduced; in it each electron has ceased to be a particle occupying a definite place and has become a wave, centered on the nucleus and filling the whole atom. Free electrons in space are like waves on the surface of the ocean, with a wide expanse and traveling in the direction in which the electron as a particle would be moving. The positive charge in the nucleus of an atom attracts the negatively charged electron wave to it and constrains it to vibrate in a fixed pattern centered on the nucleus. These wave patterns are rather like those formed by a vibrating membrane or drumhead. There are a fundamental mode of vibration and a sequence of overtone modes, as in the case of a violin string or a drumhead.

The electron waves restored a generally spherical character to atoms, but the waves themselves are so insubstantial that such an atom can scarcely be called hard, as it was in the nineteenth century. Nevertheless, it turns out that electron waves resist interpenetrating one another with strong forces. As a result, atoms collide with one another as if they were hard elastic spheres. The result is the same as that which even Lucretius visualized, but it is obtained in a way that would certainly have seemed strange to him, even weird in the extreme.

Another characteristic of atoms which the wave atom neatly resolves but which the planetary atom could not is the identity of atoms. All the atoms of a given chemical element throughout the universe have identical properties. The wave patterns formed by vibrating electron waves are determined solely by the electric force exerted on the wave by the central nucleus and so should produce identical patterns in all atoms with the same nuclear charge. In the simplest atom, hydrogen, the one electron vibrates in the lowest frequency or fundamental mode in every hydrogen atom in the universe, in its normal or ground state. This makes hydrogen, wherever it is found, have always the same physical and chemical properties, and its atoms have identical sizes and shapes.

Without elaborating, we may say that there are many ways in which the wave atom has succeeded where the planetary atom simply would not work. Within the nucleus itself, where neutron and proton waves, vibrating in discrete patterns with fundamental and overtone modes, are involved, it has been very successful, too. The extent to which this wave theory of matter, called quantum mechanics, mirrors everything we have been able to observe about molecules, atoms, and nuclei is so broad and so precise that its reality can scarcely be questioned. Yet in our search for the secret of matter it has forced on us a very strange picture indeed. These matter waves are not even waves in ordinary space, but they vibrate in an abstract mathematical space, called configuration space. They are just about as insubstantial as anything that may be imagined. Yet they give atoms their shape, size, hardness, and elasticity, and they determine the forces which atoms exert on one another in forming molecules.

Inside the Elementary Particles

At the outbreak of the Second World War it seemed that a rather complete and full understanding of matter was within reach. The triumphs of quantum mechanics in explaining the wave atom and molecules, as well as in making a most promising start on the structure of the nuclei of atoms, were numerous and remarkable. Just four elementary particles were required to account for the whole universe. One could see how the nuclei of all atoms were what they were because of the laws governing the combinations of neutrons and protons out of which they were constituted. Given these nuclei, electrons would then assemble in well-defined states of vibration with predictable wave patterns to form all known atoms. These in turn could combine in predictable and well-understood ways to form the molecules, crystalline solids, or liquids needed to account for all the manifold diversity of nature as we experience it. Added to this was the particle of light or radiation, the photon, which accounts for the exchange of energy between atoms and molecules. We had almost in hand with these four elementary constituents of matter—neutrons, protons, electrons, and photons—a nearly complete and universal picture of the structure of matter. It was, and still is, a beautifully coherent and all-embracing picture of the world.

But there were a few isolated phenomena that did not fit this otherwise universal picture. At the end of the nineteenth century the phenomena of electricity and magnetism and the existence of electrically charged atoms, or ions, did not fit the otherwise coherent atomic theory of the time. They seemed then rather minor exceptions but became the key to the next stage in depth by revealing the nuclear atom with its electrons. So at this stage what seemed to be minor exceptions to the general picture now seemed to be leading us to another and deeper level under or inside the neutron, proton, and electron.

These exceptions were the phenomena of radioactivity and the discovery of antimatter. A radioactive nucleus transforms itself into the nucleus of an atom one step higher in the periodic table of elements by emitting an electron and another particle, called a neutrino. The neutrino is an uncharged electron, which, like the photon, is massless and therefore travels at the speed of light. Its role in the otherwise neat arrangement of elementary particles was, and remains, obscure. The problem so far is unsolved.

The other exception was the discovery of the antielectron, or positron. This was the first instance of what we now know to be a general property of matter—namely, that for every particle of matter there is a kind of mirror image of it made of antimatter. A photon of sufficient energy can disappear, and in its place an electron-positron pair can materialize. Part of the energy of the photon is used to create the masses

201]

of the particle and the antiparticle, and what is left over is shared between them. When subsequently a negatively charged electron and positively charged antielectron come together, they annihilate each other, and the energy of their masses is shared between two photons which appear in the process. All the properties of an antielectron, except for its mass, are the opposites of those of an electron. The antielectron did not fit into the otherwise uniform scheme of things any more than did the uncharged electron, or neutrino.

The period since 1950 has seen a profuse elaboration of other strange particles which do not fit into the scheme of things that prevailed in the second quarter of this century. There are two kinds of radioactivity which atomic nuclei undergo. In one of them an electron accompanied by an uncharged massless antielectron (*i.e.*, an antineutrino) is emitted. In the other an antielectron, or positron, accompanied by an uncharged massless electron (*i.e.*, a neutrino) is emitted. If, however, much greater amounts of energy are available than is the case in atomic nuclei, heavy electrons or heavy antielectrons, both charged and uncharged, are emitted in preference to ordinary electrons. A heavy electron, otherwise called a muon, has more than 200 times the mass of an ordinary electron, and its uncharged complement is a distinct particle, different from the neutrino; but like the neutrino, it is also massless and so always travels at the speed of light.

The neutron and proton are now seen to be just a pair of particles in a much larger family, consisting of a lambda particle, three sigma particles, two cascade particles, and ten others. All eighteen of these particles have corresponding antiparticles, making a total of thirty-six basic particles and antiparticles. These basic particles in turn have excited states, which form a whole complex spectrum of elementary states of matter, very much like the spectra of light from atoms and molecules which were so puzzling until the wave model of atoms was developed.

In addition to this strange array of particles of matter, generally called baryons, there is another array of less massive particles, called mesons, which constitute a nuclear radiation field, much as the photon constitutes electromagnetic radiation, or light, or as another, still hypothetical particle, called a graviton, constitutes gravitational radiation. There are seventeen basic mesons and antimesons, together with a spectrum of excited states.

This complicated array of what has come to be referred to as "strange particles" is a far cry from the neat scheme of building the whole universe out of just four elementary constituents which largely characterized the first half of this century. Just as the first quarter of the century was largely devoted to the planetary atom and the second quarter to the wave atom, so it seems that this third quarter is largely concerned with the attempt to understand these subatomic strata of strange particles on which the wave atom, which makes up our familiar world, rests.

Quite recently there has been made a fascinating breakthrough which brings a great deal of order into this bewildering assortment of strange particles. It has been found that all eighteen particles of matter called baryons, including the familiar neutron and proton, can be explained by supposing that each one is a complex system of three elementary particles called quarks. The corresponding eighteen antiparticles are then made up of three antiquarks. The seventeen mesons and antimesons each are a system consisting of a quark and an antiquark in intimate association.

The quarks are very strange objects indeed. Two of them make a pair of common quarks, with a positive electric charge two-thirds that of an electron and a negative electric charge one-third that of an electron. The third, or strange, quark has one unit of a property called strangeness and a negative electric charge one-third that of an electron. The neutron and proton and four of the other strange particles are made up of only the first two, or common, kinds of quarks and so have zero strangeness. The remaining particles have one or more of the third kind of quark in them and so one or more, up to three, units of strangeness. The most common meson, a triplet of three particles called pions, are quark-antiquark combinations involving only the common quarks. Others contain either a strange quark or a strange antiquark.

All this sounds complicated, no doubt. We mention these things about recently detected quarks, etc., to impress the general reader with the intricacies of our subject matter and also to show what even our brightest scientists are "up against." The remarkable thing about quarks is that so far every effort to observe them has been unsuccessful. It may be that they are so massive that none of our present high-energy particle accelerators provides sufficient energy to dislodge one from a neutron or a proton. A major motive for building an immense 200,000,000,000-volt accelerator, about whose site selection there has been so much publicity recently, is to determine if this will be sufficient to produce individual quarks. On the other hand, it could equally well prove to be the case that quarks can only occur in combinations of three or in pairs of quarks and antiquarks. If this were really a law of nature, then quarks could never be observed singly or in pairs, but only in the combinations already observed. In that case they would remain an interesting and successful mathematical device for explaining what we do observe, but their reality and existence would remain questionable. My own opinion is that the latter alternative is the probable one and that individual quarks will never be observed. This, however, is only an opinion or hunch, and other physicists deeply involved in this question do not share it. There is no unanimity, and to that extent the problem is unsolved.

Nature has shown unexpected and amazing depths. The quest for the secret of matter has led us into one depth after another. At each plunge the world which has been revealed to us has shown strange new wonders and symmetries. At each stage it has proved amazingly intelligible to the human mind, yet in terms increasingly far removed from the obvious or familiar world of our everyday experience. J. Robert Oppenheimer in his *Science and the Common Understanding* has likened all science to a vast underground palace with an unending series of interconnecting rooms. This is an apt simile. At first, as we began to explore the antechambers near the entrance, it seemed a familiar building of limited size, much like other buildings we were familiar with. But as this century has advanced, unsuspected rooms have been entered and surprising interconnecting passageways discovered. Each new room or suite of rooms has been full of surprises, strange new beauties, and unsuspected wonders. Yet each time that we began to think that we had reached the palace boundary and were in the innermost rooms, we have stumbled on hidden doorways, which have led us into still deeper and more amazing sections of the palace.

Each question that has been answered by science has only posed several new questions. This quality of reality, by virtue of which each question about it opens up several more questions in a divergent rather than convergent series, represents genuine unfathomable mystery. It is not a question of individual mysteries capable of being cleared up one at a time. Instead, it is an overall state of affairs characteristic of the whole quest for understanding reality itself. This situation alone has introduced a sense of mystery and wonder in modern science which is quite the opposite of the spirit of science in the nineteenth century.

There are many ways in which the quest for the inner secret of matter has developed this sense of mystery. For the nineteenth century, matter possessed only the one simple property of mass. By now we recognize several independent properties in complex admixtures in different samples of matter. It is by virtue of mass that the gravitational attraction of objects takes place. Electric charge determines the electromagnetic forces on matter and is wholly independent of mass. A third property, possessed by neutrons and protons, but not by electrons (ordinary or heavy), may be called nuclearity and determines the very strong force which holds neutrons and protons together in nuclei. Another property determines the ability of matter to emit or absorb uncharged electrons or neutrinos. If quarks exist, they possess a fifth property, independent of these others, by virtue of which they exert immensely powerful forces on one another. The three common constituents of matter possess these properties in varying combinations. The electron has mass and electric charge, but no nuclearity; the neutron has mass and nuclearity, but no electric charge; the proton has all three.

Even more amazing than this variety in the basic composition of matter is the existence for every form of matter of its mirror image in antimatter. Because of this, matter and antimatter can be materialized in equal quantities and then later be annihilated. This lends an impression of insubstantiality and transitoriness to matter which is quite at variance with earlier convictions about it. This character of matter is further emphasized by the universal applicability of quantum mechanics, whereby all particles of matter dissolve and smear out into so-called probability waves in abstract mathematical space, called configuration space (see above).

The old materialism, which reduced everything to simple masses in motion, has certainly been swept away. The contemporary materialist must visualize material reality in terms of matter and antimatter waves, in a kind of shadow world, and consider them to be made up of mass, charge, nuclearity, and other basic constituents according to various recipes. It is a strange and shadowy kind of materialism, with none of the simple, substantial, and sturdy obviousness of the old established kind.

It is interesting to speculate on where the quest for the secret of matter may ultimately lead. If quarks exist and individual quarks are in time observed, a question about them will remain: Are they the ultimate elementary particles of nature, or is there a still deeper level which describes what quarks are made of? On the other hand, if quarks have no individual existence, then what? An alternative to quarks has been suggested. I myself have an idea. But at the moment it is tentative.

There is a considerable drift in today's thinking toward the kind of shadow world I have referred to. The mysterious probability waves, as well as the complementary relationship of matter and antimatter, may be mentioned in this connection. The aura of mystery which surrounds the whole question of the secret of matter seems now to be a permanent characteristic which no conceivable future research is at all likely to dispel.

In connection with the present discussion we may think of David who in Psalm 145 says that the greatness of the Lord and His works is unsearchable. One of the meanings of the word translated as "unsearchable" is "mysterious," and we are certainly finding it out, even 3,000 years after King David's time and even after all the exhaustive research of recent decades. One who deals with matter, *any* matter, is, in the words of the Apostle Paul, dealing with "the deep things of God." (I Cor. 2:10, AV)

FACING UP TO SOME VERY
MODERN MYSTERIES

BY TERRY F. GODLOVE

ELECTRICAL ENGINEER
RESEARCHER IN MAGNETICS

Dr. Godlove is one of the great scientists in the service of the Federal Government whose names one doesn't often find in newspapers or magazines, but upon whose expertness and zeal so much depends for the safety and progress of the country. They are usually very well known and greatly respected in their own high scientific circles. With a B.Sc. from Lafayette College and an M.Sc. and a Ph.D. in physics from Yale University, this scientist went directly into Federal service. He is presently the head of the Accelerators Section, Linac Branch, Nucleonics Division of the U.S. Naval Research Laboratory, Washington, D.C. He is a member of the Physics Society and the Research Society of Nuclear Physics and is widely known among scientists as a specialist in electronics and particle accelerators.

ENGLAND's great poet John Milton speaks somewhere in his poetry of "all nature's works" and describes them as "deep secrets all." Milton's great mind often was absorbed in these secrets. They made him sense deeply his own paltriness and insignificance and the towering greatness of nature's God.

Since Milton's time a great many of nature's secrets have been unveiled, brought into the open. But every honest scientist will admit that even in this second half of the twentieth century the secrets of natural science are still multitudinous and that many of nature's mysteries are still so heavily veiled that their disclosure seems next to impossible. Yet it is a comfort to know that the Lord has used scientists of every description to enrich our modern lives with interesting, useful, and even highly exciting discoveries. He is still "a revealer of secrets." (Dan. 2:47,AV)

In the present chapter of this book I wish to make a few very brief observations about two different subjects: fundamental constants (electrodynamics) and thermonuclear power. I shall couch my material in plain, nontechnical language.

Fundamental Constants

Some of the more fundamental questions in electrodynamics carry an aura of mystery. Consider the electrostatic charge on the electron, the lightest and in some respects the most fundamental of all particles. The electron may be free, as it is when it sails from an electron gun to the screen of a T.V. set, or it may be in orbit around a proton in a normal hydrogen atom, or it may be dancing along a copper wire from pole to pole through the neighborhood.

Scientists have measured the charge on the electron and its gravitational mass many, many times and in many environments and always get the same answers. Of course, the accuracy is pushed to another decimal place every few years, but basically it appears that the values obtained are fundamental and immutable constants of nature and, as far as we can tell, have been so since the origin of the universe. The same statement applies to the velocity of light and a few other constants.

These are the sorts of numbers which sophomore physics students write on the inside of their book covers and memorize for examinations. The student intuitively senses that it would be foolish to ask the teacher why the electron has that particular charge or mass. There is no reputable theory which can explain or predict why the electron should have the particular charge or mass that the God of nature has endowed it with. Once these quantities are measured and known, the *behavior* of the electron in countless applications is absolutely predictable, at least in a classical sense. The point to be noted here is that the behavior in any application ultimately depends on knowledge of the fundamental constants. Yet any scientific and reliable explanation of the constants, their origin and fixedness, has not yet been given. They are, as of today and from the viewpoint of science per se, enigmatic—an unsolved problem.

Of course, this and similar problems are on such a deep level that only a comparative handful of scientists are really thinking about them. It may be that a future Einstein will discover and formulate a new, more profound law of nature which will account for some of the fundamental constants. Very likely such numbers will then no longer be called fundamental, and some of the mystery will be gone. But history teaches that even if this happens, the new law will contain its own constant or constants, perhaps fewer in number than before, yet still unexplainable and just as mysterious in their own right. In other words, the frontiers will be steadily pushed back, but there will always be frontiers.

The situation is perhaps analogous to that existing in cosmology (theory of the cosmos as an orderly system). Many astrophysicists are working, for example, on the big bang theory of the origin of the universe. It's a truly fascinating subject of study, encompassing astronomy, nuclear physics, thermodynamics, electrodynamics, and other fields of science. Let's take it for granted for a minute that this theory is correct, that a certain glob of nuclear matter really started with a certain energy at a certain point in space at a certain time, billions of years ago. The teacher tells his students this. What will happen? A student may whisper under his breath, "Were you there, professor?" But actually and openly he will ask the ultimate question: "Why is it and how is it that the universe started with those particular initial conditions?" The scientist will still, after a moment of silence, have to use words something like those of the Apostle Paul: ". . . we see through a glass, darkly." (I Cor. 13:12, AV)

Thermonuclear Power

One of the most intriguing unsolved problems of today is generation of power from thermonuclear (heat plus nuclear) reactions or, as it is more commonly called, taming the hydrogen bomb. Just as the H-bomb is capable of much more destructive power than the A-bomb, similarly thermonuclear power far outstrips atomic power in its theoretical peacetime potential. This problem dates back to the development of the H-bomb in the early 1950's and involves several fields, mainly classical electromagnetism, plus nuclear physics and classical atomic physics. (Classical in this connection means in accordance with generally accepted and therefore authoritative principles and methods.)

What does thermonuclear power mean? For an answer to this question, first recall that fission, used for atomic power, involves the splitting of a heavy nucleus, like uranium or plutonium, into two medium-size nuclei, accompanied by the emission of energetic neutrons. Some of the neutrons cause other heavy nuclei to split, giving rise to the well-known chain reaction, which continues automatically when once started. Power is then generated by making use of the heat from a carefully controlled chain reaction. The basic physical principles were known for many years. Most of the effort in the development of commercial power was spent on such problems as the most efficient way to transfer the heat, the proper choice of materials, and safety features.

In contrast with the relatively straightforward development of atomic power, the efforts to tame the H-bomb have been anything but straightforward. In order to understand

211]

the difficulties, we must consider the reaction itself. In essence two nuclei of hydrogen come together at high velocity and *fuse* to form a larger nucleus, releasing energy in the process. The *heavier* isotopes (atomic species) of hydrogen work best, but for simplicity we use the word "hydrogen" to denote any of its isotopes. The important point is that the hydrogen nuclei must fuse at high velocity. This means, in terms of a quantity of hydrogen gas, that the entire gas must remain at an extremely high temperature, even millions of degrees, in order that the agitation caused by the high temperature be sufficient to give the hydrogen nuclei high velocity.

This in turn leads to the gargantuan task confronting the scientist. There is no ordinary container, not even the material used for satellite heat shields, that can withstand a nuclear fireball. The temperatures of such a fireball are the temperatures that occur in the interior of the sun, since the reaction is the same one as that which gives the sun part of its energy.

We can now see the major difference between atomic power and thermonuclear power. The chain reaction of atomic power can occur at ordinary temperatures, and reasonably ordinary materials can be used for containers. The thermonuclear reaction occurs only at extreme temperatures and is a true burning of nuclear fuel. In an H-bomb, part of the released energy sustains the high temperature until the fuel is exhausted. But for peaceful power some way must be found to control and contain the fireball.

Scientists soon realized, after the initial flush of optimism had abated, that this problem might be exceedingly difficult to solve. It was as if the Devil had conspired to allow only destructive uses for man's application of the fusion reactions.

The problem has been attacked primarily with the trick of magnetic containment. As the name implies, this means the employment of suitable magnetic fields to provide the walls of the chamber. A magnetic field is capable of bending charged particles, such as hydrogen ions, and the shape of the magnetic field can be arranged so that the ions (electrified particles) always bend back toward the center of the fire-ball, or plasma, as it is usually called. The goal of the scientists is to achieve the containment of plasma, not only at a sufficiently high temperature, but also with a sufficient quantity of gas and for a sufficiently long period of time. The last requirement is important because it turns out to be rela-tively easy to produce a hot, dense plasma which lasts only for a few millionths of a second. It is the combination of high temperature, high density, and long duration which has so far eluded the scientists. This is, for the present at least, the great unsolved problem.

And a great problem it is! Thousands of scientists and engineers in many countries have applied their talents to this problem, and many millions of dollars have been spent. I can think of no other peacetime problem, save the exploration of space, on which so much effort has been spent. At this writing the ultimate goal of thermonuclear power is not yet in sight, but a tremendous amount of by-product knowl-edge has been gained about plasmas and hot gases.

The main obstacles have been the various instabilities suf-fered by hot plasma. A good example of an unstable plasma in nature is found on the surface of the sun. Tremendous masses of hot gas move in a highly turbulent manner across the boiling surface of the sun. Occasional jets of gas are thrust out thousands of miles into space and sometimes curve slowly back onto the surface. These are instabilities on a grand scale.

At the other extreme, scientists have found many in-stabilities on a microscopic scale. It would seem that lurk-ing in the shadows of every plasma laboratory lies an undis-covered instability, waiting to pounce on unsuspecting scien-tists that are trying out a new device. Hot plasmas simply don't care to be contained.

What is already known is fantastic, much stranger than fiction. What is unknown is awesome. A personal and pur-poseful God would be a small god indeed if there were not unanswerable questions behind every truth or fact which man discovers. Unsolved and even unsolvable problems are bound to remain. The ancient paradox confronts us: We were created "a little lower than the angels" (Ps. 8:5, AV), yet with a great gap between our mind and knowledge and the mind and knowledge of God. But the man of faith keeps pursuing knowledge, not because he expects to receive an answer to every ultimate question or a solution to every tenacious problem, but because he is happy in the confidence that God is encouraging him to share in the process of learning and discovery, to master nature, to use his power wisely, and by and through it all to benefit humanity and, primarily, to magnify his Maker at beholding an ever greater display of his Maker's creative might.

ABOUT FOSSILS AND THE BIRTH
OF MOUNTAINS

BY CLIFFORD L. BURDICK

GEOLOGIST

*The editor knows this writer as a man of great techni-
cal knowledge and experience. After being graduated
from Milton College, in Wisconsin, and gaining his M.Sc.
degree at the University of Wisconsin, he did extensive
studying at the University of Arizona and became a min-
ing geologist in the United States and Canada, followed
by step-by-step advancement. Today he is a well-known
consultant in geology. He has published more than fifty
papers in the fields of geology, paleontology, and nuclear
geology and has lectured repeatedly at the University of
Arizona.*

UNSOLVED problems—the field of geology teems with
them. This profusion has led to much theorizing by brilliant
scholars, theorizing about the origin of the earth, its constituent elements, the manifold changes it has undergone, and so
forth. Many of the theories have suffered an easy death.
Others are still up and about, some of them marching bravely
to the accompaniment of much applause, others sort of limp-
ing along, and again others just standing, joints weakened
and a sickly pallor over their faces.

Almost from the beginning of time men have sought to

explain the origin of the earth. But we shall not let all those long millennia pass in review. Let us go back 100 years, for just a fleeting glance. About a century ago it was the nebular hypothesis that held sway. Many scientists taught that our world and other worlds were condensations of material from a giant fiery celestial spinning wheel. This theory remained prevalent in certain circles until mathematicians discovered the physical impossibility of such a genesis.

Other theories came to the fore, but the vacuum left by the nebular hypothesis was not filled until Chamberlin and Moulton's planetesimal hypothesis was advanced. According to this hypothesis a celestial body of enormous size had come so close to our sun that a part of its substance was torn away and resulted in a number of tiny planets, which by gradual accretion grew to the size of our present planets, including our own planet.

This theory also was soon found to be untenable. Again we let pass certain other hypotheses or theories. At the present time a number of astronomers at Mount Wilson and Mount Palomar suggest that the universe is a closed system which *pulsates*. And Dr. Sandage of Mount Palomar thinks that the universe, hence our earth, may have originated with a terrific explosion of very dense nuclear matter which is now expanding in all directions in the form of stars and galaxies.

The point I am trying to drive home is that with all our high-powered telescopes and with astronomers and physicists and mathematicians of the first rank wrestling with cosmic problems, many scholars seem as far from arriving at a reliable cosmogony (theory of the origin of the universe) as ever, although it must be readily admitted that they are constantly gathering important data from fresh observations for other useful purposes. In fact, some of their speculations appear to be leading farther from a solution than before. In my own thoughts I am close to Dr. A. Cressy Morrison, former president of the New York Academy of Sciences, who stated that the universe shows such definite design and purpose that it demands a Master Mind to account for its

[216

many perfections. That, of course, holds true of our earth as well.

But I attach greatest importance by far to the testimony of God himself. There is one part of the Bible that was written directly by God. All the rest of the Scriptures were put down by inspired writers. But one small portion God himself wrote, with His own materialized, fleshly hand. It is the Ten Commandments. Here is the excerpt I have reference to: "In six days the Lord made heaven and earth, the sea, and all that in them is." (Ex. 20:11; Deut. 5:22, AV) The psalmist echoes this when he says, "The sea is his, and he made it; and his hands formed the dry land." (Ps. 95:5, AV) Once again the Creator himself confirms it in His question to the suffering landholder of Uz: "Where wast thou when I laid the foundations of the earth?" (Job 38:4, AV)

So much for the mystery of the origin of things physical. Another unsolved mystery in both geology and paleontology (the science that deals with the life of past geological periods) is the widespread and evidently sudden extinction of animal life in the past. This extinction did not happen, as is true of the present slow fading of the condor bird or the buffalo (bison), because of the activities of human hunters. Mesozoic life (referring to an ancient geological era) was dominated by a great variety of large reptiles, well adapted to their environment and able to compete with anything, inasmuch as the mammals of the time are considered to have been quite small. But in the Gobi Desert we find a veritable graveyard of large reptiles—dinosaurs, perhaps running into the millions. I have seen dinosaur graveyards in New Mexico and their romping grounds in Texas. A Utah dinosaur graveyard looks extremely peculiar—as if the beasts had congregated in herds when they saw some sudden disaster approaching. Scientists as a rule have no adequate explanation for all this. They admit that the mighty reptiles that ruled the earth in Mesozoic times were well adapted to their environment, and it is a mystery to them that there should have been such a wholesale extinction of so many types.

It is almost axiomatic in geology that for the perfect preservation of fossils there must have been sudden burial; otherwise the carcasses would have been destroyed by scavengers or by bacterial action. The British scientist Hugh Miller was amazed at the perfect details in the fossil fish which he found in the Old Red Sandstone of England. Some had the fins extended as if in fright or fear of attack, or as if some sudden catastrophe had come upon them. In the New York State Museum, at Albany, may be seen some 400 starfish which died in the act of devouring clams—a thing one would hardly expect in a natural dying-out process. An animal too weak to live any longer could hardly be expected to go foraging for food. The presumption would be that some catastrophe had suddenly overtaken them.

Perhaps the most striking example of sudden death and extinction is that of the frozen mammoths of Siberia and Alaska. This subject is of such importance that it really deserves more than a casual reference. Several books have been published about these animals. Here is not just one mystery, but a whole string of them. How could vast numbers of mammoths meet extinction so suddenly and be frozen so quickly that the flesh was preserved without decomposition? Together with the mammoths, and in the same condition of preservation, were wooly rhinoceroses, horses, giant oxen, tigers, giant bison, wolves, and beavers. In the case of some of the mammoths, freshly bitten grass and buttercups were still in their mouths! A sudden and enormous natural upheaval of some kind? Scientists have made many guesses, but so far none has gone beyond the realm of fancy. There is no solid historical or geological object for them to grasp hold of. They're really at a loss.

The Beresovka find was perhaps the most spectacular of all. A mammoth was found at about the turn of the century by a Siberian tribesman. It was sticking headfirst out of the bank of the Beresovka River, which empties into the Arctic Ocean. In its mouth was still a portion of its last meal, which for some unknown reason it had not had time to swallow. The meal was composed of delicate sedges and grasses and, most amazing of all, fresh buttercup flowers. The stomach contained many quarts of similar food, without a sign of decomposition, so swiftly had it frozen. If this was the work of a long, long ago blizzard, it certainly could not have been an ordinary one—perhaps an extraordinarily violent hurricane with winds 100 degrees below zero (F.). The mammoth was still upright, but it had a broken hip, as if it had been catapulted against a tree or a bank. Otherwise its exterior was intact and perfect. Its shaggy fur was in place. It was squatting on its back end, with one front foot raised as if to raise itself into a full standing position after having been dashed against some obstruction.

One is struck by the suddenness, the instantaneousness, of all these happenings. One is also struck by the incongruity of the situation: finding these ancient animals eating food that belongs to the temperate zones, eating it in the arctic stretches of the Siberian tundra, northern Alaska, and similar barren regions. In our imagination we see vast herds of large well-fed beasts, placidly feeding in sunny pastures, plucking buttercup flowers in balmy temperatures, and then suddenly frozen to death, quick-frozen, frozen so rapidly and thoroughly that every cell of their bodies was perfectly preserved, despite their great bulk.

Is this, too, an unsolved problem, one of the greatest? The generality of scientists say it is. But I am not quite ready to go along with them. I'm inclined to believe that the climate of these northern regions suddenly changed, as suddenly as when the mammoths and other animals froze in their tracks. It wasn't only the animals that froze; we have evidence from fossil *plants*, too, indicating that formerly semitropical plants were growing in these cold barren regions, even above the Arctic Circle.

Where do I get this seemingly freakish idea? I get it from the Bible account of the Great Deluge, the Deluge of Noah's time. Many of us know that the Bible is not the only source of Deluge information. The Gilgamesh Epic of ancient Mesopotamia, the records of the kings of ancient Sumer (later Babylonia), and the mythology of the Mayas and other ancient peoples—all carry references to the Great Deluge. But the Bible alone, as I see it, gives us the true and authentic account. The Book of Genesis tells us that the Lord was going to send rain upon the earth forty days and forty nights, and it quotes the Lord as saying: ". . . and every living substance that I have made will I destroy from off the face of the earth." Genesis also reports: ". . . the same day were all the fountains of the great deep broken up, and the windows of heaven were opened." (Gen. 7:4,11, AV) The Deluge was a cataclysm of such enormous violence and proportions as the world had not seen before and has never seen since. The most potent proof of its radical nature and appalling magnitude and frightfulness, I think, is the testimony of Christ when He compared the end of the world with "the days of Noah." (Matt. 24:37-39, AV)

Toward the end of the Deluge, God caused terrific winds to blow, gradually making the earth dry again. Although it is not specifically mentioned in the Sacred Record, the Deluge was perhaps also *preceded* by hard winds, just like those which we ourselves have witnessed in the case of minor rainstorms. The winds may have come suddenly and may have been unimaginably and destructively cold. The Deluge was a *punitive* measure.

Such a general catastrophic event as the Deluge may have caused permanent changes in the earth's climate so that formerly temperate regions became frigid and barren. The water and vapor in the atmosphere tend to act as a thermal (heat) blanket. Before the Deluge the blanket must have been thick and heavy. Genesis speaks of "the waters which were above the firmament." (Ch. 1:7, AV) After the Deluge the heat blanket became flimsy in comparison, and frigidity resulted in northerly places. This should cast a measure of light on the fossils question, although many minor problems still remain.

Then there is the problem of the ice age, or the glacial ice caps which covered much of the Northern Hemisphere during the Pleistocene period (immediately preceding the present geologic period). In North America there were at least two centers of dispersion: the region of the St. Lawrence River and the western mountain ranges, together covering about 5,000,000 square miles and thought to have reached a thickness or depth of around 10,000 feet. Many northern states—especially Wisconsin, where this writer was brought up—are covered deep with glacial drift. Only this past summer, on a trip back there, it was interesting to study the erratics, rocks strewed about the landscape that had been transported from farther north, even from Canada.

The great and still unanswered question in connection with the ice age is, What caused it? Yes, there have been attempts at explanation. Some have thought of a shifting of the poles. Others have suggested other natural changes or derangements. Perhaps the most popular explanation among geologists is that of volcanism—that the upper atmosphere was so full of volcanic ash that a considerable portion of the sun's radiation was absorbed before it reached the earth. It must be admitted that certain other explanations seem plausible. But, as stated, that of volcanic ash has garnered most of the scientists' votes. So, if we limit ourselves to this interpretation, what caused the volcanism? Some say a disturbance of the isostatic balance (equilibrium, or equal pressure) of the earth's outer crust, causing severe earthquakes and a multitude of volcanic eruptions. But what caused this disturbed balance? And what caused the earth's crust to settle down to near perfection, as it is today, and the volcanism almost to cease, and the atmosphere to clear, and the ice sheets to vanish, except for the ones located in the polar regions and among the highest mountains? Must we, after all, look back to the Deluge, its action and aftermath?

An encouraging thing has happened recently. One of our leading paleontologists (scientists who study life in past geologic periods), Dr. Norman Newell, of the American Museum of Natural History, in an address to the American Geological

221]

Society in New York made the statement that accumulated evidence of cataclysmic geological events in the past is forcing us to reappraise our former strict adherence to a theory that would judge the geologic past by the present. He concluded by saying that in the future catastrophism must take a larger place in our geologic thinking. This writer is ready to shake hands with Dr. Newell on that anytime.

The unsolved problems in geology are legion, and when some reputable geologist comes forward with a solution, there will very likely be a geologist just as reputable to refute his explanation. There is, for instance, orogeny, or the origination of mountains. As we can easily observe, mountains are not distributed evenly over the face of the earth but usually occur in clusters, separated by plains or hilly terrain. How have they come into existence?

In the nineteenth century James Hall and James Dana developed the contraction theory, based on the idea of a cooling earth, with the interior shrinking faster than the already cool crust and leaving the crust or outer garment of the earth too big for the core it was covering. The natural result would be wrinkles or mountain ranges—like a drying apple with a wrinkled skin. About the time that almost everyone had accepted this hypothesis as axiomatic, serious objections began to appear. The concentration of radioactivity in the crust of the earth suggests that the crust has *not* been cooling!

Some scientists proposed the theory of drifting continents. Their idea was that in the far-distant geologic past all the continents were joined together, then split up and drifted apart. In the process of drifting, contractions were supposed to have occurred, resulting in mountain ranges. The theory foundered for several reasons, but mostly because of the lack of an adequate motive force. What caused the continents to split, and what set them in motion?

Another hypothesis was that of convection currents (motions resulting from heat or differences of density). It was assumed that the earth's rock at great depths is hot and highly plastic. If one heats tar over a fire, the hotter tar at the bottom will rise and displace the cooler tar at the top. If the tar were to flow from the edges of the container toward the center, there would be a thickening and rising, simulating a mountain range. This, like several other theories, has run afoul of many technical difficulties.

There are a few facts in connection with the origin of mountains that we can be fairly sure of, although connected with every fact are many problems that still await solution. The facts are that many mountains are the result of faults in the subterranean rocks; that others are the result of a set-tling process of the surrounding outer earth crust; that others resulted from powerful volcanic action, causing ter-rific pressure from below; and that still others were the effect either of a slow and prolonged erosion or of a quick-action and violent erosion by a cataclysm—the Deluge.

But there are also the mountains that were produced by direct action of the Creator, at the beginning of time. It would take a detailed study to single them out. But *created* they were, undoubtedly to reflect the power and majesty of God. My authorities for this information are three great Bible figures: Moses, Solomon, and Isaiah. All three of them have connected the "bringing forth" of mountains with the creation of the earth. I am told that the original Hebrew lan-guage brings that out more clearly than the translation. (For Moses, see Ps. 90:2; for Solomon, see Prov. 8:25, 26; for Isaiah, see Ch. 40:12.)

As stated before, the science of geology confronts us with a thousand problems. Human ingenuity and effort have solved many of them. Others, no doubt, will continue to be solved in the same way and by the same means. Still others seem entirely unsolvable. It is a good thing to know that an all-provident God stands back of it all. Nothing among the activities of nature just happens. If it did, and on any ap-preciable scale, this cosmos would have been knocked or blown to smithereens long ago.

Some of our problems have been solved for us through special revelation—the Bible. There is, to mention just one more example, the phenomenon of interbedding, the alternation of distinctly different types of rock strata, like, say, a 2-foot-thick layer of limestone, then sandwiched in between it and the next layer of limestone a thinner stratum of shale or perhaps sandstone. It is not uncommon to see this alternation of strata multiplied many times in a rock exposure, like the stripes of the American flag. An unusual and huge example of this is the Morrison formation, a portion of which I once mapped along the Arizona-New Mexico border. This non-marine continental rock stratum averages about 400 feet in thickness and covers some 100,000 square miles in Montana, Utah, New Mexico, and Arizona. Since it is a nonmarine formation, what agency could have deposited this tremendous sheet of rock? Science doesn't know, may guess at it, but doesn't know. Only the Deluge could account for it.

Again the Deluge! Genesis 8 says that when the Lord was ready to dry up the floodwaters, He produced a strong wind to blow the waters to and fro, no doubt with hurricane force and, according to the record, for many months. Swiftly moving water has terrific erosive power, as well as transporting ability. No doubt the wind was caused to blow now from one direction, then from another, accounting for the different types of rock deposit. This is assuming, of course, that the Deluge was worldwide, an assumption apparently sustained by the Sacred Record.

This writer was listening to a leading American geologist sometime ago, and he heard the astonishing statement that about 90 percent of geology is still in the realm of speculation. The figure may have been a bit high, but it emphasizes the uncertainty of many geological ideas and conceptions that too frequently are being taken for gospel truth. There is ample room for academic freedom, for an opportunity to air one's personal views. In this chapter I have made use of the opportunity.

THE PLANET THAT BECAME
OUR TEMPORARY HOME

BY HAROLD S. SLUSHER

GEOPHYSICIST

SEISMOLOGIST

The writer of this chapter is widely known as a high authority in geophysics and seismology (the science of earthquakes). He is the director of the Kidd Memorial Seismic Observatory, in El Paso, Texas. With a B.A. in mathematics from the University of Tennessee and an M.Sc. in physics from the University of Oklahoma, he studied and researched his way upward until he achieved his present prominent position. Additional fields of research, related to his specialties, have been geodesy and tectonophysics, and Professor Slusher continues his activities in these fields. He also teaches geophysics and astronomy in El Paso, at Texas Western College, a division of the University of Texas.

THERE is solemnity, even majesty, in the very opening words of the Bible: "In the beginning God created the heaven and the earth." This repudiates atheism, for it postulates the existence of God, and refutes materialism, for it distinguishes between God and His creation. This all-important statement also informs us that He is a personal being, for an abstraction could not create. It argues that He is infinite and omnipotent, for no finite being could create the universe.

God has created a universe, complex, marvelous, mysterious. The universe shows us the art of God, and "the invisible things of Him since the creation of the world are clearly seen, being perceived through the things that are made, even His everlasting power and divinity; so that they may be without excuse." (Rom. 1:20, RSV) The Book of Job says, ". . . speak to the earth, and it shall teach thee . . ." (Ch. 12:8, AV), and the geophysicist does this by performing experiments on the earth and studying its physical characteristics. Geophysics provides the exciting and adventurous quest for new knowledge, laying bare things invisible beneath the earth.

Modern industrial society is very dependent on the location and use of natural resources, such as petroleum, minerals, and water. From all the geophysical exploration that has taken place, it would seem that all the major problems of the earth would have been solved by now. This is far from true. We still do not really know why continents are where they are; how mountain ranges originate; whether earthquakes cause volcanoes, or vice versa; or even whether the earth is heating up and expanding or cooling down and contracting.

Very few are aware of some of the fascinating, unexplained observations of geophysics. For example: Mountains are not strong enough to support themselves but appear to float on the mantle (middle section) of the earth. The earth is divided into: (1) the crust, (2) the mantle, and (3) the core. Mountains have roots, so to speak. The crust is thicker under mountains (sixty kilometers) than under continents (thirty kilometers) and than under oceans (ten kilometers). A kilometer is about five-eighths of a mile. Two-thirds of the crust is covered with oceans, and these oceans contain the highest and longest known mountain ridges and the deepest trenches.

Some of the rocks now exposed at the earth's surface are suspected of originating at depths as great as 300 kilometers, where the pressure exceeds 100,000 atmospheres. These rocks

[226

resemble fragments of some meteorites that have collided with the earth.

Neither earthquakes nor volcanoes are randomly distributed in space or time but are concentrated in known belts. There are about 10 earthquakes each day, together equivalent to a 5,000-ton atomic-bomb explosion.

The unsolved problems facing the geophysicist are legion. Most earth features have not been adequately explained in terms of present-day processes. The science of the earth is an astonishingly inadequate thing, in which little has actually been demonstrated. Let me cite a few cases of real difficulty to back up my contention. These problems are very important in geophysics.

One of the most important unsolved problems is that of mountain building. This is certainly very basic to any real understanding of the earth. I believe that the major structural features of the earth's crust are associated with the forming of the mountains. Very recently, in terms of world history, the orogenic (mountain-building) processes seem to have been immensely active. The data seem to prove that man lived during the time when deposits which are now found on top of the mountains were being laid down and that, therefore, the mountain-making processes, with all the attendant phenomena, have been active in comparatively recent times. They are not active now, at least not measurably so. And men have left no record of past orogenic events. Yet the processes associated with mountain building and their results are considered by geophysicists to be absolutely basic to the interpretation of earth history. Here, then, is an extremely important gap in our knowledge.

Many believe that there has been more than one cycle of uplift and submergence of sedimentary strata (fossil-bearing rocks formed from sediments) in forming the mountains. A major difficulty is the concept of sedimentary processes found in areas of very thick deposits which have gone through one or more cycles of uplift and submergence, yet have beds or layers of rock that remain marvelously horizontal and continuous. Strata (layers) laid down by water are, of course, in a horizontal position. Yet we may now find some of the strata standing on edge, like books on a shelf. All human experience shows that they were not deposited in this position. Some great disturbance must have occurred since they were laid down. What is the answer?

A good example of the action of water is found in the Colorado Plateau, where the distinguishing characteristic is the approximate horizontality of its rocks. This beautiful conformity seems hard to account for with all the supposed cyclical movement of land and sea. What are the facts?

Then there is another problem. A given mountain range could not have been elevated until the very latest of the layers composing it had been laid down by the waters as sediments. The interesting thing in this connection is that by this principle about all the mountains have to be called very young, as practically all of them contain Tertiary, or even Pleistocene, strata. Most of the great mountain chains could be listed as illustrative examples. What could account for the uniformity or simultaneousness of the uplift of the great mountain ranges?

A question arises of what has caused the uplift of sedimentary masses forming the mountains that rise to heights of thousands of feet above the general land level. The crust of the earth is very irregular and is made up of mountains, canyons, basins, rifts, oceans, continental masses, and many other topographic features. The earth's crust may very roughly be divided into two levels: a continental one about 3,000 feet *above* sea level and an oceanic one about 13,000 feet *below* sea level. Why do not the continents sink down until the entire crust is at the same level? Their weight is immense, and the underlying material is somewhat elastic and would yield to this weight.

Let us dig a little deeper into these problems. Inferences from gravity data have led to the principle of isostasy (equal or balanced weights). The credit for the discovery of this principle rests mainly with the geodesists because of their analytical studies of gravity measurements. The principle of isostasy proposes that the major topographic features of the earth are associated with internal inequalities of density, so that the high portions maintain their position by "floating" on an "effectively liquid" subcrustal material. In other words, an excess of mass above sea level (as in a mountain system) is compensated by a deficit below sea level so that at a certain depth, known as the depth of compensation, the total weight per unit area is equal all around the world.

The isostasy principle, which has a most important bearing on tectonophysics (structural features of the earth), is based on the idea that the higher areas of the earth's surface, such as mountains, uplands, and plateaus, are balanced against the adjacent lowlands. Each great block of the earth's crust (say, of a magnitude of about 100 miles on a side) is supposed to be in a state of gravitational balance with every other such block.

The term "isostasy" means equal weights. The weight of any great area of the earth's crust of some certain size, including water and air over it, is always nearly the same as the weight of any area of equal size, whether this be mid-ocean, mid-continent, over low plains, or in mountainous regions. But this condition of isostasy does not always hold true for certain places of a limited area.

Let us suppose a group of high mountains, sometime in the past, whose rivers flow into an inland sea. Both areas will normally be in a state of isostasy: The weight of the earth's crust in one place balances the weight of the crust in the other. But rock weathering and river flow have their effect, and after a while most of the material is laid down on the inland sea floor. Unless something yields, the crust where the mountains once stood will be of much less than normal weight, and the crust of the former inland sea will be greater in weight. Despite the solidity of the earth's crust, it is thought that there will be a sufficient flow of the material deep down in the mantle so that the surface with the surplus mass will sink until it reaches a state of approximate isostasy, and the denuded area will be pushed up until it reaches the same condition.

Think of the Rocky Mountains, although any other great sedimentary mountains would do as well. The Rockies are composed of sedimentary rocks that are thousands of feet thick, yet reach a very high altitude in the United States and Canada. Supposedly there once was a depression, in the United States, in which rivers could lay down the load of material that was later to become the sedimentary rocks forming the mountains. This should make the surface of the depression sink more and more as more sediment is added to it. Instead, this vast amount of matter has been raised thousands of feet above the general land level. This is a reverse of what would be expected according to the isostasy principle. Yet this principle, as determined from gravity data, is sound and logical. So the vital question is, What can cause the uplift of the sedimentary troughs to the great heights of the layers that we observe in high mountain regions? Have our scientists, after all, interpreted things correctly? Or are we facing problems that lie beyond human ingenuity?

There have been many hypotheses put forth regarding the origin of the earth and its structure. These hypotheses hinge very strongly for support on certain ideas regarding temperatures within the earth and the initial temperature of the earth at its creation.

Temperatures are measured within the earth's crust by placing elaborate thermometers in deep wells and mines. From such measurements a change of temperature of $1°/F.$ for every 60 feet of depth is concluded. Now, if this temperature change with depth is used to calculate the temperature at the center of the earth, an absurdly high value of $350,000°/F.$ is obtained. Evidently this method cannot be used to determine center temperature. It may, however, be indicative of very high temperatures within the earth.

Many observations have been made regarding heat flow from within the earth, since this gives clues to internal temperatures. It is found that these values obtained over land and sea are remarkably uniform and come to be about one-millionth of a calorie per each square centimeter of surface per each second of time. The very significant thing about this is that there is no difference between continental and oceanic heat flows. This obviously suggests that each square centimeter of the earth's surface is underlaid by the same amount of heat-generating radioactive matter. This is strange, since it is known that the continental rocks contain much more radioactive matter than the oceanic rocks. We are certainly facing a paradoxical problem—an unsolved problem.

Some attempts at explanation of this seeming paradox have been made. There are those who believe that the mantle under the oceans is hotter than it is under the continents. But this is objectionable since a required 500°-1,000° F. temperature difference is too large not to be detected. Another view has it that the radioactive matter somehow migrated from the mantle upward to the continental crust, but not to the oceanic crust. This would require a transmission process similar to convection currents (up-and-down air movements) in a room, for instance, in which different parts are at different temperatures and cold air moves around to force out warm air. This would mean that the composition of the mantle is very fluid. It is known, however, that S waves (shear waves) from earthquakes, which can only be transmitted in solids, travel through the mantle of the earth, so it is hard to imagine it being fluid enough to have convection currents. Therefore, this explanation, too, is unsatisfactory. We are again confronted by an unsolved problem.

This also raises an interesting question about the cause of deep-focus earthquakes (those between a depth of 70 kilometers and 300 kilometers). What, really, is an earthquake? Most evidence points to a sudden movement of solid rock along faults in the earth as the cause of earthquakes. Such faults in many cases are scars of earlier fractures, which occurred when the stresses, developed within the earth, became too great for the rock to support. An additional stress, if large enough, may cause slippage, and this slippage in turn sends out shock waves that may be felt over thousands of square miles on the earth's surface. This would be a major earthquake.

As far as the earth's interior is concerned, an earthquake is, in many respects, like a vast explosion which sends out vibrations everywhere. In order for the energy to be released in the sudden manner that is necessary to cause an earthquake, the energy must be stored in matter rigid enough not to release it in a slow and gradual manner. This causes a discrepancy in respect to the mantle. From the viewpoint of seismology (the science of earthquakes) the earth's mantle is regarded as solid; from that of isostasy (see above) it is regarded as fluid. Attempts have been made to harmonize these divergent concepts, but the attempts have not proved satisfactory. Man has never had an opportunity to explore the earth's mantle, and it is still a matter of much wonder what the actual state of the mantle's material is. Another problem!

In a study of the earth temperatures it is interesting to look at such matters as heat sources and sinks. There are actually two possible heat sources: radioactive matter and chemical reactions. The sinks are usually moving underground waters.

The temperature of the earth at any point located below a depth not subject to surface periodic variations remains constant for all practical purposes. Owing to the great mass and heat capacity of the earth, temperature changes caused by heat losses alone would amount to only $1°/C.$ over a period of a possible 10,000,000 to 50,000,000 years. When consideration is given to both radioactive heat sources and general heat losses, there may even be an *increase* in temperature of perhaps $30°/C.$ in a possible 1,000,000 years— that is, if the radioactive mineral values at depth are of the order of the minimum values at the surface. Although the percentage of radioactive material in surface rocks is small, if such material is scattered throughout the earth with the same density, the total collection would be enough to supply many times the amount of the yearly loss of heat. In fact, the heat generated would be so great as to necessitate the assumption that radioactive materials exist to a depth of only a few miles of the surface shell.

From a human viewpoint this whole matter of heat distribution poses a sticky problem. How did it come about? Who arranged it? Who or what controls it? For those who accept David's statement that "The earth is the Lord's" (Ps. 24:1, AV), the answer lies within easy and immediate reach.

The other source of internal heat is chemical reactions. This source may be due to the oxidation of ore bodies (combination of ore bodies with oxygen) or some other form of alteration. It may also be due to the oxidation of hydrocarbons (compounds of hydrogen and carbons) that escape from oil reservoirs within the earth.

Professionals who happen to browse through this piece of writing may be interested to know that some careful measurements were taken over a sand lens in a location in Kansas giving a temperature difference. Some simplifying assumptions were made for the calculations, and it was found that this temperature difference could be maintained by a heat source generating one ten-millionth of a calorie per square centimeter per second. When certain physical properties were assumed for the sand lens, it was shown that to generate continuously the heat needed to maintain the temperature difference, all the oil would be oxidized in about 3,000,000 years. This result is in no way in agreement with well-known popular conclusions about the age of the earth. If the oxidation of hydrocarbons is a major source of internal heat, then the postulated values for the age of the earth will have to be drastically altered.

It is interesting to note in passing that the age of the earth comes out much less by using present erosion, deposition, or accumulation of soda in the ocean than by the methods

233]

based on the rate of uranium decay (which, by the way, gives many very anomalous, dissimilar ages). The motto "The present is the key to the past" comes in for some examination. By the way, the uranium decay method is now in turn open to question, since it has been shown that the decay rates can be changed by external effects.

The geophysicist is like a detective trying to piece together many strange pieces of a most interesting puzzle. The unsolved problems discussed in this chapter are but a very few of the many in this field. There are many others that are mysterious, challenging, and important.

To this geophysicist not only do "the heavens declare the glory of God" and does "the firmament (show) his handiwork," (Ps. 19:1, AV) but the earth also manifests His infinite knowledge and accomplishments. At the same time one begins somewhat to understand why the Bible fairly exhausts its language in magnifying Christ, of whom it is said that God "created all things by Jesus Christ" (Eph. 3:9, AV), and who is called "the beginning (originator or first cause) of the creation of God." (Rev. 3:14, AV)

Zoology

OUR MODERN FIGHT AGAINST
TWO ANCIENT DISEASES

BY WILBUR L. BULLOCK

ZOOLOGIST

PARASITOLOGIST

Dr. Bullock is a man both of learning and of experience. He was graduated with a B.Sc. in biology from Queens College, New York City, and with an M.Sc. and a Ph.D. in zoology from the University of Illinois. Since 1948 he has been on the staff of the University of New Hampshire and is now a professor of zoology. But, he advises us, "my teaching and research interests are particularly in the area of Parasitology." For several years both the National Science Foundation and the National Institutes of Health have cooperated with him in his scientific endeavors. Dr. Bullock has been a visiting professor of biology at Rice Institute and at Florida Presbyterian College. He has done extensive research at the Mountain Lake Biological Station, of the University of Virginia, and at Woods Hole, Massachusetts, for the U.S. Fish and Wildlife Service. He is faculty adviser for the Intervarsity Christian Fellowship at his own university.

GREAT masses of people—millions of them perhaps—are dying every year because of unsolved problems—problems that learned men all through the ages have eaten their hearts out, so to speak, and racked their brains to solve, so far with only limited success. Before we enter on that tragic subject, may I be allowed a question or two and make some observations that will lead right up to our subject?

The writers of the Bible, when they observed nature, recognized God in it. They saw His mighty acts and took notice of His incomparable greatness. That greatness was obvious everywhere. Modern man has far more knowledge of these mighty Divine acts than his ancient predecessors. At times, however, he seems unaware of God's very existence. Let me ask these questions: Why are so many modern men unconcerned about the greatness of God? What would happen if modern men, including those who, as "Christians," consider themselves godly, regained the proper respect and awe for the majesty of Him who "made heaven and earth, the sea, and all that in them is?" (Ex. 20:11, AV)

I believe modern man's indifferent attitude has much to do with our failure to solve certain very pressing problems in the domain of nature. King Solomon, in ancient times, asked his son if he wanted knowledge and understanding, and then told him that if he really "meant business" to go to the Lord. He said: "For the Lord giveth wisdom; out of his mouth cometh knowledge and understanding." (Prov. 2:6, AV) I am thinking in this connection of the Lord's own direct statement that "them that honor me I will honor. . . ." (I Sam. 2:30, AV) I doubt that the Lord will pour out His blessings of knowledge and understanding on those who tacitly—and sometimes not so tacitly—ignore Him.

Modern man is unconcerned about God's greatness for many reasons. Perhaps the most important reason is that so many people today put God out of their lives completely and live for pleasure, material gain, or intellectual achievement. At best, many people will marvel at the beauties of nature with no concern for the Creator of nature. There is a proud fascination with all the problems we have solved, all the things we have learned, all that we are able to control. Even the *unsolved* problems become a challenge to the power and the ingenuity of man, rather than a source of humility. God has become, at best, a mere onlooker at the triumphs of man.

How can man, under these conditions, become aware of God's power and majesty? Respect for the greatness of God is primarily the result of a genuine spiritual faith. It is the result of a deep faith in the God and Father of our Lord Jesus Christ as the Creator of the universe. We may sing "How Great Thou Art!" but we do not always integrate our science and our theology. Too many men, I am afraid, have allowed themselves to be brainwashed into thinking and acting as if the Bible writers praised God only because they were ignorant. Now that they know that winds are caused by interaction of high-pressure and low-pressure systems and that diseases are caused by microorganisms, it appears that God isn't important anymore.

Nothing can be further from the truth. Just as the sacred writers praised God in the known and the unknown, so must we put our achievements in the right perspective and recognize that even what we know came to us through the merciful providence of God. Although human knowledge is increasing at an astonishing rate, we must still realize that what we know is only a very minute part of all there is to know. Most important, we must not take a weak defensive position, whereby we continue to give man the credit for the known and permit God to become great only as the God of the unknown, the "God of the gaps." God is great, and God is to be praised in the known as well as in the unknown. As the psalmist has it: "Great is the Lord, and greatly to be praised; and his greatness is unsearchable. One generation shall praise thy works to another, and shall declare thy mighty acts." (Ps. 145:3,4, AV) Let us apply these truths and facts as we examine, briefly and rather cursorily, one small area of biological knowledge in which much has been accomplished in recent years, an area that still challenges us with many unsolved problems.

❉   ❉   ❉

In the matter of disease man and animals have much in common, as we shall see. Diseases among animals are a prolific source of certain widespread and frightful diseases among men, and, in a certain measure, the converse is also true. Our understanding of the biological nature and significance of disease in man and animals is an area of knowledge in which our perspectives on the wisdom and greatness of God have become overshadowed by our human preoccupation with immediate causes. It is commonplace to hear people today reason as follows: "Before mankind knew about the relationship of bacteria, viruses, and parasites to disease, primitive man ascribed sickness to the anger of God (or the gods). Now that we know about microorganisms it is obvious that God has nothing to do with the presence or absence of health." Such reasoning is even ascribed unjustifiably to the Bible and used as evidence that our modern secular knowledge has superseded the wisdom of the biblical writers. But have microbes really displaced God?

One of the most important diseases of man is dysentery. This sickness, which is still a scourge in underdeveloped areas of the world, has been described and referred to since ancient times. King Jehoram of Judah, who murdered his brothers to capture the throne, was told by the Prophet Elijah, "Behold, the Lord will bring a great plague on your people, your children, your wives, and all your possessions; and you yourself will have severe sickness with a disease in your bowels, until your bowels come out because of the disease, day by day." (II Chron. 21:14,15, RSV) Today we know, through the work of countless microbiologists, parasitologists, medical doctors, and others that the immediate cause of dysentery is a variety of pathogenic (disease-causing) microorganisms, including viruses, bacteria, and amebas. The last mentioned are protozoa, one-celled animals, similar to but really different from the familiar amebas of ponds and biology classrooms. It is our understanding of these amebas that we want to consider in some detail, in

[238

order to see some of the complexities that develop even when we think problems are being solved.

The first vague indication of an association of amebas with disease was detected by Lambl just a little more than 100 years ago. It wasn't until 1875 that a reasonably good description of the parasite we now know as *Entamoeba histolytica* was given by Loesch. This description of the parasite was from a case of amebic dysentery in what was then the city of St. Petersburg, Russia. The following 25 years saw considerable progress in substantiating the concept that certain amebas caused dysentery. As the result of serious epidemics of amebic dysentery during the Spanish-American War and in the Gallipoli campaign of World War I, further detailed studies were made of this disease. The German microbiologist Fritz Schaudinn in 1903 clearly showed not one but two different kinds of ameba from the human intestine. One of these, *Entamoeba histolytica,* caused dysentery; the other, *Entamoeba coli,* was completely harmless. By 1919 the British protozoologist Clifford Dobell had not only confirmed the existence of these two species but also added three more: *Endolimax nana, Iodamoeba williamsi,* and *Dientamoeba fragilis.* All these new species were completely harmless or nearly so.

Now that the species of amebas living in man had been identified, it would appear that all that was necessary was to prevent people from getting into contact with them and to develop effective drugs. Not only did these two problems prove formidable, but the research of the last 40 years also seems to have raised more problems than it has solved. Although there is little question about the identity of the four harmless species of amebas, there are a number of unsolved problems concerning the pathogenic one, including its very identity. For example, we now know that although 15 percent or more of the world's population is infected with *Entamoeba histolytica,* fewer than 1 of every 10 of these infected people actually have amebic dysentery. In other words, 90 percent of the people who have this organism living in their intestines are not made sick by it or at least do not show the symptoms of real dysentery. Many of them show no symptoms whatsoever.

That there are size strains of this protozoan has been known for some time. It has further been determined that the larger the strain, the more pathogenic (disease-producing) it is. In actual dysentery the amebas are usually 18 to 25 microns in diameter (a micron is 0.000039 inch). In symptomless carriers the amebas may be only 5 to 7 microns, and there are numerous in-between strains. Currently there is a tendency to call the very small ones a separate species— *Entamoeba hartmanni*—but this still leaves the large and small *Entamoeba histolytica*. The large ameba is thought of as a disease-producing form that invades the intestinal tissues, while the smaller one appears to be a harmless form that lives in the intestinal lumen (tubular passageway).

But can the harmless one become dangerous and invade the tissues? If so, under what circumstances? Should everyone who has anything that looks like *Entamoeba histolytica* be subjected to the sometimes drastic treatments for this parasite? Do laboratory technicians have to be instructed in much more difficult diagnostic procedures? These are unanswered and controversial questions because of the inadequacy of our understanding of "simple" amebas.

Some insight into the complicated nature of this problem comes from work done on an ameba of reptiles. This interesting ameba, *Entamoeba invadens,* looks very much like *Entamoeba histolytica* but will not grow in warm-blooded species, such as man. It is also the only other known disease-producing ameba in the animal kingdom, although in other animals there are many kinds of amebas that appear to produce no disease. *Entamoeba invadens* lives in turtles but produces no disease in them. In snakes, however, this ameba often causes fatal amebic dysentery. Studies of this ameba in snakes have shown that different snakes are affected to different degrees. The green snake is hardly affected at all, but water snakes are very severely affected. It was further found that the temperature at which snakes are kept has a profound effect on the outcome of the infection. In snakes kept at 13° C. there is little tissue invasion and, therefore, little dysentery, but snakes kept at 25° C. (approximately room temperature) develop serious dysentery.

These few fragments of information should serve to indicate that the problem of amebic dysentery and how it is produced is very complicated. Indeed, we are just as puzzled by the question of why several types of amebas can live in the intestine and *not* produce disease! Although volumes have been written and there are hundreds of current research projects to investigate various phases of this disease, we still know very little about how amebas can live in the human or animal intestine; how some can cause serious and even fatal disease; and why different species of host animals and often different individuals will react differently to the same strain. These are all problems—and many of them.

But dysentery is not the only disease in which we find a bewildering complexity of solved and unsolved problems. From a universal, public health point of view, there is no disease that can compare with malaria in terms of total number of cases, total number of fatalities, and extent of land areas made uninhabitable or unproductive. Even though the disease was associated with swamps long before Ronald Ross (1857-1932) proved the mosquito to be its vector (carrier) and quinine was recognized as an effective antimalarial drug, it was not until World War II and the subsequent World Health Organization that remarkable and even fantastic successes were scored against this dread disease.

Most malaria transmission was found to be associated with a habit of the main mosquito involved. The effective transmitters all rested on the walls of houses after their blood meal. The use of DDT on the walls of the houses (so that the insecticide would remain effective for a considerable time) drastically reduced the incidence of malaria in many areas. Elaborately organized malaria-eradication programs

241]

were so successful that malariologists spoke with enthusiasm of the complete elimination of this disease from the face of the earth by 1970. This looked like one of the most remarkable victories against any disease. While there is no question that the world has, in recent years, been more free of malaria than it has ever been, in the last decade a few sour notes have been sounded to mar a beautiful story.

In many areas of the world the structure of the houses is so primitive that there is more open space than solid wall. Such houses complicate the problem by their very shape. Besides, the inhabitants frequently move to new houses that have not been sprayed for some time. Then other problems appeared in certain areas. In these areas closer investigation yielded evidence that transmission of the parasite was now carried on by mosquitoes that did not rest on the walls of the houses to digest their blood meals. Rather, they flew outside to areas that had not been sprayed with DDT. In addition, it was found that mosquitoes were becoming resistant to DDT and other insecticides. Recently it has become known that some of the malarial parasites themselves have become resistant to chloroquine and the other synthetic drugs that have been successful since World War II. Drug-resistant malaria has been reported from a number of areas but seems to be worst in Southeast Asia, including Thailand and Vietnam. Most disturbing of all, this resistance has been most prominent in the malignant tertian type of malaria (a type in which paroxysms occur every third day, inclusively figured). Consequently, in a few years we have had to turn from an enthusiastic overoptimism to a somewhat grim realization that the fight against this disease is not over. Besides, the years of optimism about malaria eradication have caused a shortage of well-trained malariologists to meet the new threat.

We have seen, in two of the most serious diseases of mankind, that formidable problems remain to be solved. These problems remain in spite of great advances in our understanding of the causes of the diseases, the methods of prevention, and the required treatment. The problems remain in spite of millions of man-hours devoted to them and billions of dollars spent on them. While we can and should be impressed by all that biologists and medical men have learned about these problems, we should humbly recognize our great limitations.

One of the principal things that Christ did while on earth was to heal people of their physical diseases. That was prophetic of large-scale action to come. While we encourage professional men to do their utmost to eradicate disease, let us expect lasting, all-encompassing deliverance from the Lord of Life.

THE MYSTERIOUS LAWS OF MATTER AND ENERGY

BY JOHN A. BUEHLER

CONSULTING CHEMIST

Dr. Buehler is well known as a consulting chemist to important industrial corporations. He has also been a frequent lecturer on highly technical subjects for the Indiana Academy of Science. After graduating with a B.A. from the University of Pennsylvania, he obtained an M.A. and a Ph.D. from the University of Indiana, where he majored in organic and inorganic chemistry. Dr. Buehler was a professor of chemistry at Anderson College, and is presently serving in the same capacity at LeMoyne College, Memphis, Tennessee. He gained his scientific laurels and was widely heralded for his detection of Cobalt II by succinimide and isopropylamine.

THE last 100 years have been a period of phenomenal development in the science of chemistry. Especially rapid has been the advance since the turn of the century, when a major breakthrough occurred in our knowledge of the structure of matter. The discoveries by Crookes, Thomson, Becquerel, and the Curies in the last part of the nineteenth century and by Rutherford, Bohr, Moseley, and others during the early part of the twentieth century enlarged our knowledge of atomic structure.

The Daltonian concept of the atom as a solid core and as

the ultimate particle of matter was shown to be erroneous. The atom was found to be dynamic and made up of many subatomic particles, around twenty-four in kind. Quantum mechanics was developed to explain the behavior of such minute particles as electrons, protons, and mesons.

With a clearer understanding of the structure of matter, theories were developed to explain the formation of compounds, the structure of crystals, the formation of color, the solubility of compounds, and the chemical and physical properties of the elements. Many of the phenomena in nature that had baffled the chemists—such as the distribution of the electrons around the nucleus of the atom, the reasons that certain elements react and others do not, the ways that macromolecules in nature are put together, and many of the biochemical functions of the body—were solved by the invention of new tools of research, such as X-ray diffraction, mass spectroscopy, infrared spectroscopy, and magnetic resonance—just to mention a few.

As new techniques were discovered to study the structure of matter, many of the mysterious diseases gave up their secrets. Tailor-made compounds were synthesized to combat malaria, spasms, insulin deficiency, and many abnormal functions of the body. Thus, by 1965 the chemist felt that almost any problem was solvable if enough time and money were available to investigate the phenomena.

Having accomplished the total synthesis of such complex molecules as quinine, strychnine, lysergic acid, many of the vitamins, amino acids, and hormones, the chemist was ready to put his final touches on the synthesis of proteins, the riddle of life. For several decades researchers concentrated their experimental know-how, utilizing their latest theories and scientific instruments, to unravel the mystery of life. Ever since the vitalist theory was overthrown by Wöhler's synthesis of urea, in 1826, the chemist approached the solution to his chemical problems in a mechanistic manner. This approach to the problems that confronted him proved to be successful, and one mystery after another was solved. He began his attack on the mystery of life with the conviction that there was nothing "vital" in life. If the proper combination of atoms could be arranged in their correct sequence, life would be created.

The problem centered on the structure of the nucleic acids. After many painstaking experiments by hundreds of researchers the nucleic acids were finally broken down and their component parts identified. The general structure of the DNA and RNA molecules was determined, and a three-dimensional structure of the molecule was elucidated by the work of Watson and Crick in 1953. Man was on the verge of breaking the genetic code.

At the present moment it seems highly probable that man will someday be able to start with the elements and construct molecules that will be able to reproduce themselves. Does this mean, then, that we have no need of a vital force outside ourselves and that God isn't really out there in "the dim unknown" with His Divine unceasing activity? Could it mean that all the vital forces in the universe reside in matter and energy? Unfortunately, this is a viewpoint held by many who in the past held to the idea of God because they had gaps in their theories which needed a God to explain the gaps. As the gaps were closed, one by one, by the advance of knowledge, and as more and more of nature's secrets were unraveled and yielded to painstaking research, there was less and less need for an all-powerful Creator. But just assume that man did succeed in unlocking the mystery of life, and just suppose that he would actually be able to produce cells and then multiple-celled creatures—would this rule out the idea of God as Creator?

If we analyze what man has accomplished thus far, we see that he has only discovered the laws that govern the elements. He hasn't created the known existing elements. He hasn't made the laws that govern the behavior of the elements. Behind the elements are the subatomic particles. They also obey laws. Someday man may be able to put together subatomic particles to create elements. If he does, he will have to become acquainted with all the laws that govern these particles. He will be confronted by a great many unlooked-for problems!

Frankly, I marvel chiefly at one phenomenon of nature, and that is *law*. What is law—natural law? How did natural law come into existence? Is there someone who made the laws that govern matter and energy? Is there a lawgiver?

When we recognize God as the Lawgiver, then we need never fear the possibility that someday man's advance in knowledge may fill some gap we now have. *I postulate that man will never make a universal law of nature.* Man can only discover the laws that already exist and then use these laws in a meaningful way to unravel the structure of matter and, once having unraveled the structure, to synthesize that structure from the elements or maybe someday from the subatomic particles.

To understand how natural law is related to God, to appreciate the extremely finite nature of the human mind, and to make one realize that humility befits even the brightest among modern scholars, one can do no better than make a careful survey of chemical science—its history, its struggles, its disappointments, and its victories. Such a survey is bound to convince a student of the reality of nature's laws and consequent order and design. Only by postulating a directional force with a purposeful end can one account for what one beholds. This is even evident in the order among the atoms. There is a definite pattern that is followed from hydrogen to uranium and beyond.

God is infinite; we are finite. Much of our difficulty in evaluating observable facts is due to our limitations. Du Noüy has said that our scale of observation is oftentimes wrong. A gram of carbon black when mixed with a gram of white flour would appear to us gray, but to a microbe crawling through the pile it would appear as a pile of black and white boulders. His level of observation is different from ours.

But our scale of observation and other characteristics belonging to our finite nature should not obstruct our view of nature's fixed laws and of the God who established them. There are many things in nature that are at present unexplainable and shrouded in mystery. We are surrounded by problems. We will, of course, not make the same mistake the ancients made when they conceived of gods to explain the unexplainable, assigning to each god his power and function. At a later stage, as science developed and many of the mysterious phenomena in nature became understandable and as the laws which governed their behavior were discovered, gods were no longer deemed necessary. For many even God became superfluous.

Instead of considering God, or the idea of Him, superfluous or instead of classifying Him among the so-called unknowables, we should see and adore Him in the mysterious, all-comprising, never-and-nowhere-failing natural law. That law, in its countless ramifications, brings us closer to understanding God. God uses that method to reveal himself to us. This method is often called His *general* revelation. It is not His only method—there is His *special* revelation in the Bible —but it is an important one.

THE ENIGMAS OF PSYCHOPHYSICS

BY RALPH F. COLEMAN

NEUROPATHOLOGIST

Psychophysics is the science of relations between mental and physical processes and phenomena. Today this science is closely connected with such other new sciences as biophysics, bionics, cybernetics, biomedical engineering, and medical sciences of a neural or behavioral type. Dr. Coleman has for many years made a specialty of the relationship of the seen and the unseen, the physical and the nonphysical, the body and the mind in our human existence—a specialty that had been waiting for ages to have men of high capability devote their attention to it. Dr. Coleman is one of a comparatively small number of scientists that have done so. He has M.Sc. and M.D. degrees, and is a professor of neuropathology at the University of California, at Los Angeles (Neuropsychiatric Institute and Brain Research Institute, U.C.L.A. Center for the Health Sciences), and is a member of numerous important science groups.

As all my readers know, the word "enigma" means a riddle or a problem, and I am using the plural of the word in the title of this chapter because there are so many problems in the science under discussion. The terms "brain" and "mind" can be used interchangeably in our discussion because structure and function are one and the same as long as there is life in a person.

Several questions spring to mind as soon as such subjects as brain and life are mentioned. For instance, can scientists eventually create life, artificially? Can life, ultimately, be prolonged indefinitely? Can the human mind be artificially controlled? Can scientists develop techniques which will enable man to alter the intelligence, personality traits, and behavioral patterns of other humans *without their cooperation?*

Then there are questions of another nature: Should scientists do these things? Can a person who believes in God do these things and feel morally justified? Should Christians or other believers in God who are not scientists actively support, or ignore, or condemn research which is concerned with the brain and nervous system? Should we ignore the fact (perhaps not generally known) that such research work is being strongly supported in Russia, and that mind-controlling weapons are not fantasies but probabilities of the near future?

The atom has been harnessed, space travel is now a reality, and another reality is the fact that the mind is already giving up its secrets to neuroscientists, who are employing the recently developed techniques of biophysics, environmental medicine, aerospace medicine and engineering, physiology, biochemistry, electronics, biology, and the modern behavioral sciences, as well as medicine, engineering, and other disciplines. The brain did not answer questions for metaphysics; for a long time it was an enigma to psychophysics; but it speaks readily when questioned by the researcher who employs the scientific method, recent technological advances, and some of the recently developed concepts, such as control and adaptive system analysis, auto- and cross-correlation analysis, and information and communication theory, to name only a few.

There are, of course, many unanswered questions in our field, many unsolved problems, many serious doubts—for example, about the solution of such an everyday, yet colossal, problem as how our nonphysical thought life can influence our physical substance, and the converse. But I believe that we—scientists and nonscientists, believers and nonbelievers in God—can arrive at some worthwhile, reliable, meaningful opinions if we are willing to consider, with honesty and without emotionalism, both the problems and the related facts now available. Such a presentation is neither intended nor possible in a writing such as this, with its limitations of space. I will, however, present some of my personal views. Some of the reasons for my tentative opinions should become apparent as I touch on some of the accomplishments, methods, anticipated achievements, and difficulties germane to the scientific search for understanding of the mind and control of the mind.

Speaking of understanding and controlling the mind, I believe that it is important to know just who these people, these scientists, are who would struggle to bring forth such a perplexing problem. Some of them are morally good; some may not be. All of them are curious about themselves and their world. Is not every human creature? But the great question is, What actuates their curiosity; what moves and incites them; what are they after? Have they an ultimate goal? What is the nature of that goal?

Man is innately curious about life and its significance. His curiosity has caused him to search (and research) in hope of escaping the dissatisfactions of the present and of obtaining a future of knowledge and freedom from discontent. But, as Landor said, "let us descend from generalities to particulars." What is it that makes men dissatisfied with the present, and what constitutes for them that desirable future? Answers would vary with the great variety of individuals, with the great variety of scientists, too. Let us get back to what all true scientists have in common, regardless of their faith, philosophy, and purpose in life.

Let us ask if there is any demonstrable evidence of the soul, the mind, consciousness, thought, sensation. The answer is that only partial answers are now available. Modern medical science considers the mind and the living physical body inseparable parts of the whole person. Now, thanks to the recent advancements in technology, adequately controlled scientific investigations within the neurosciences are providing information which suggests that for every behavioral manifestation there is both a physical and a mental phenomenon. Several years ago investigations, related to splitting the atom, established that mass and energy are forms of the same thing. Matter is never destroyed, it is only changed. Which comes first, the thought or the related electrochemical activity within the nervous system? Or are they one and the same? At present we do not know. We may know tomorrow.

The techniques of biophysical (not psychological) research relating to the behavioral and medical sciences will undoubtedly help scientists establish many more verifiable relationships between physical and mental phenomena in the future. (One hopes that this will be in the *near* future, inasmuch as mental institutions are now overcrowded by the psychotherapeutic failures.)

During the past few years brain research (psychophysics, neurophysiology, etc.) has been greatly enhanced by the development of methods and techniques such as high-speed electronic, transistor, and solid-state recording systems, radiotelemetry, and techniques for utilizing adaptive systems analysis. Adaptive systems are already used in pilotless aircraft, space explorations, and industry. Will we be able to study and identify the complex adaptive systems which exist in continual activity in man?

It has been established that the brain (nervous system) is constantly active during life. In the brain this activity operates in many ways, one of which is the formation of bioelectrical currents which occur in rather specific patterns (brain waves) in normal individuals. These electrical patterns can be recorded and measured by an instrument called the electroencephalograph (E.E.G.). The E.E.G. is a valuable diagnostic tool. It has answered many questions for medical science, but it has also created questions. For example, studies with the E.E.G. have demonstrated that a normal part of sleeping is dreaming and that rapid eye movements (R.E.M.) are associated with the dreaming. Investigators who have carefully studied this phenomenon(Dr. William C. Dement, for instance, of Stanford University) believe that the R.E.M. period (dreaming which lasts for approximately twenty minutes and occurs about every one and one-half hours of normal sleep) represents a third biologic state. During these R.E.M. periods the brain may show activity similar to that observed during the waking state, and the eye movements follow patterns similar to patterns used in daytime activities. Does man *look* at the contents of his own dreams? Does he look at his own inner world? Or is he watching another world, outside himself? Or does he see a mingling of the two? What are the facts in the case?

Then there is telekinesis, which means the moving of objects by thought, without physical contact. Is there actually such a thing? If you had asked me that question when I was a medical student, I would have said, Probably not. Today, with some qualification, I must say that it is possible. Thanks to the space age methodology, it is now possible to detect, measure, and modify the bioelectrical currents that occur in the brain, in the peripheral nerve, and in bone and muscle. Scientists in this country are now perfecting artificial limbs that will be operated electronically by coded signals from the nervous system. The Russians have in production an artificial hand that is automated and controlled by the thoughts of the amputee. So, to the question of whether thought and muscular power can be transmitted at a distance, an affirmative answer must be given. The Soviet physiologist L. L. Vasiliev says in a recent book of his that in the near future we shall be able to make use, at a distance, of instrumentally amplified radio waves that orginate from the brain, heart, and muscles, and that this ability will prove useful for many kinds of practical needs. My readers will

253]

understand that the scientific technique of all this is very complicated and that a description of it must, of course, be omitted here. But I did want to pass on the good tidings.

Studies performed on bats and dolphins led to the development of radar and sonar. Will scientists be successful in discovering the sense-of-direction mechanisms used by birds, insects, turtles, fishes, and whales? What produces detectable, if apparently transitory and minor, psychological and physiological irregularities after rapid travel through time zones, as those which have been noted to occur (according to the preliminary results of an F.A.A. study) *only* in east- and west-bound flights? Will it one day be possible to alter or disrupt the actions, consciousness, and subconscious activities of man by externally controllable forces, through the use of special types of radio waves or by inducing (modifying) electromagnetic fields? Could brain waves or bioelectrical currents be scrambled in a manner analogous to scrambling the Voice of America radio waves? Fantasy? Yes, at the moment. But then, so was space travel not so very long ago.

We must remember that although established scientific facts do not themselves become obsolete, conclusions and explanatory hypotheses based on such observable and verifiable facts *must* be continually tested and, if necessary, modified or revised in the light of new knowledge. In science there can be no ultimate conclusions! They must always be tentative. Yet from a study of our historical records, both ancient and recent, it is obvious that both the scientist and the nonscientist find difficulty in accepting the fact that, as has been said, even unwelcome truth is better than cherished error.

From studies of the biological feedback systems in man, using the communication and information theory concepts developed at the end of World War II, we can learn how man makes decisions based on perception and sensation, modified by memory and judgment. Information from such studies has already demonstrated that man controls and modifies his own input of sensory signals, meaning that the things which he perceives and understands are modified and distorted, by himself, before they reach the brain. This means that we shall have to rearrange our thinking and theories of sensation and perception.

Might this suggest that the perception disorders (mental disease) or distortions which occur in certain toxic conditions are a result of sensory signal distortions before the signals reach the brain (emotional storage centers)? We must not forget that not very many years ago the mental institutions were filled with patients who had "dementia." The "dementia," however, was cured and the emotions were found "not guilty" when the medical scientist produced scientific evidence indicating that "dementia" was not a mental disease in itself, but was a manifestation of the organic disease pellagra, resulting from a deficiency of riboflavin, a vitamin. Until the psychoanalytic contenders offer scientific proof to support their theories on the etiology (cause) of the psychoses (mental derangements), medical science must continue to look for the etiology. In the living organism neither structure alone, nor function alone, nor isolated factors can provide a study model comparable to the integrated system of the intact functional unit—man. Recently developed automated engineering systems are now being perfected for investigating the sensory-motor, cognative, and adaptive systems in man. Can the physical and psychological characteristics of man be reproduced in a machine? Some of them, probably. All of them? Hardly. Can a machine be taught to love, to respond with kindness to mental and physical suffering? In no way.

In seeking to unlock the powers of the mind, to find the causes and cures for diseases and personality or behavioral problems, scientists are seeking knowledge about that which is not yet known. This does not disturb them. Scientists could not see atoms, yet they split the atom. When I was a college student, we laughed at the foolishness of the alchemist who wanted to transform some low-grade metal into gold. Foolish! But new elements have indeed been made by the twentieth-century scientist as he has used the proper tools and techniques.

In medical school I was told that the pineal gland, thymus, and appendix were vestigial organs without purpose or function. In the face of a nineteenth-century persisting dogma, doubters of this theory got nowhere with their questions. But the doubters kept on doubting and questioning—and researching. Today we know at least this much: The pineal is some sort of biologic clock apparently regulating sex-gland activity, and it is a gland that converts a nervous input into a hormonal output. We also know that the thymus forms certain antibody-producing systems.

Will man eventually be able to discover the complete *modus operandi* of the brain (mind)? Nobody knows. But we're hoping.

Is there a possibility that man, being what he is and after sufficient mental and scientific development, will eventually destroy himself and all that pertains to him? Let us remember that not everything that is done in the name of science is done for purely scientific purposes—no more than that everything done in the name of Christianity is Christ-like.

But I don't believe in a final man-directed catastrophic ending of our far-spread scientific endeavor. I believe God would prevent any such outcome. After all, this is *His* world. I *trust* Him.

In the meantime, I seek to continue humbly to do my bit for science and to join my like-minded brothers in the medical service in expressing love for God through faithful labors for and among His human creatures. There is a deep and wonderful satisfaction in that.